40p

D1412712

# NIGHT LIGHTS

Leon Levson, *Johannesburg.*

# NIGHT LIGHTS

TWO MEN TALK OF LIFE
AND LOVE AND LADIES

by

SEYMOUR HICKS

CASSELL
AND COMPANY LTD
London, Toronto, Melbourne
and Sydney

*First Edition - June, 1938*
*Second Edition - July, 1938*

*Made and Printed in Great Britain by Wyman & Sons Ltd.*
*London, Reading and Fakenham*
738

TO

GLADYS MITCHELL

AND

TO THE MEMORY

OF

A GREAT GENTLEMAN

# ILLUSTRATIONS

# CONTENTS

## PART I

## PART II

## PART III

# PART I

## Two Men Talk

# NIGHT LIGHTS

" WHAT'S the matter ? "

" I'm a fake."

" Well, aren't we all ? "

" Perhaps, but it's foul to be fully alive to the fact that you are really unbelievably ignorant."

" What do you mean ?  I've never seen you at a loss for an answer."

" Exactly !  That's why I say I'm a fake.  I don't pretend that as a rule I am unable to side-track a main issue by getting a laugh off it, but being an alibi-merchant of that kind is nothing to be proud of ; it only means that I have spent my time flinging mental sticklebacks at real people so as not to give myself away.  I'm a fake."

" No, you are painfully sober and consequently a trifle dull."

" Dull I may be—tight I am not.  It's easy for you to sit there smiling—you are so certain of yourself, but can you imagine what it's like to find yourself swimming in deep water the moment you meet really well-read men and immediately collect an inferiority complex as large as Hyde Park ? "

" Inferiority complex because you're among people who have acquired knowledge by laborious study ?  My dear good fellow, I can conceive no one indulging in the luxury of diffidence, except in the presence of a truly creative artist. The capacity for acquiring learning is a thing one may admire

3

much as one delights in looking at an abnormally large sponge, but other than that it can suck up more water than its smaller brother, why write an ode to it ? The world is full of human sponges who drip when they are squeezed by conversation, but don't forget that their dripping is only possible because of the meats great men have baked for them. Good heavens, do have a little perspective. Take off your hat by all means if you want to exercise your arm to anyone who has given something to mankind, but never to the cat burglars of literature. They are at best only unskilled labourers."

" They always make me feel like ten cents."

" Do say fivepence. These Americanisms are like wood beetles. They are eating into the rafters which support the structure of Dr. Johnson's temple. I hate them."

The two men who were talking had just finished dinner. The restaurant which they frequented, and in which they ordered the best champagne they were allowed to owe for, was, as usual, quite full, while its band was almost as loud, and its lights nearly as low, as the dresses of the ladies who went there to eat and remained to dance.

They were about the same age—fifty, and, therefore, had sense enough to know that the gastronomic march is only for those who do not appreciate the fact that good wine needs a quiet resting place, and that when a sole-au-gratin meets a partridge-au-choux for the first time in a gentleman's stomach they should be allowed to make each other's acquaintance without being unduly bustled or flung at each other's heads.

And so the two friends sat, as was their habit, remote from all, like a pair of Eugene Arams, enjoying the Present, wondering if there could be anything more ill-bred than to regret their Pasts, and never by any chance discussing their Futures.

One, the journalist, was tall and smartly untidy, or, as he himself described his clothes, " shabby Ascot."

Years of Bohemia, with its first nights and last nights, its late nights and its new Knights, these latter being the least attractive part of it, had long since made a dusty pastel of what was once an Oxford immaculate. And this was all to the good, for real poise is only to be obtained in well-worn clothes.

His pre-war manners were an open sesame to all and sundry, while his heart, with its many scars, made him attractive even to the women he had left, and being a man of the world he had always elected to do this when they became difficult or what was far worse—too affectionate.

"Old wine and young women " was his motto, and though once possessed of a private income which had long since gone the way of all racing investments, he bore no one ill will. Not even the moneylenders, who had, as he humorously declared, once put him on his feet by taking away his motor-car.

His companion, the middle-aged moaner who had dubbed himself a fake, though he would have struck anybody who had called him one, was of quite a different type. Never good-looking, his face, unlike his florid friend's, was of the inquiring type with eyes as alert as those of a terrier in a rat pit, and an upper lip on which the seal of St. Patrick had been firmly set. A Jack of all trades and master of none, he had no real reason to be discontented with life.

Of money he had had never too much, but then again seldom too little. He was lucky in his friends and fortunate in his enemies, loving the former with the same intensity with which he hated the latter.

That he could be cruel only meant that almost on the instant he would be kind. Many women had been attracted to him and had seriously considered being true to him because he had made them laugh when as good women they should have shed tears.

But as with his faults or virtues we are not concerned, and meeting him only as an inquirer, an anvil upon which he was content to allow his friend to beat his superior brains, all that need be said of him is that he was neither better nor worse than his fellows. His Christian name was Edward.

The journalist, amongst other things, was known as Alf, though no one, himself included, quite knew why as he had been christened Stanislaus.

After Alf's illuminating remark about sponges, Edward sat silent for a moment and surveyed the crowd about him, who walked so elegantly to the noise of a group of silver-plated saxophones, behind which sat various young men with temporary brains and permanent waves exuding artificial vitality, and seeming to gain the greatest satisfaction in accompanying one of their number who, at intervals, informed the dancers through a megaphone that the tunes they had just heard were called either " In my shack at the top of the world with Mamie " or " My cocktail baby loves her sugar Daddy," both being the finest lyrical efforts of famous Broadway writers. One of the most popular fox-trots played on this particular evening was called " Asterisk," dedicated by the composer to all those who make a hobby of ice-skating.

" Is it a sign of age, Alf," mused Edward, " that I find myself getting more and more to like talk after dinner better than love after eating ? "

" Not a bit, dear fellow," replied the florid Alf. " It only

6

means that quality has stepped in where quantity once trod, that's all. When we were young the rustle of even an alpaca petticoat led us to destruction. But a sense of value does not denote impotence. All that has happened is that we have come to realize that good talk is better than an indifferently good woman, and also that we have wisely learned to find a time and place for everything.

"In our early twenties on a spring-time night when the moon was high in the heavens, we watched with the lady of our fancy its journey over the tree tops, but in the roaring forties we are not so prodigal in our waste of time.

"For myself I have made a golden rule which I observe religiously, and it is this; if I decide to visit the most attractive woman of my acquaintance, and I go to her knowing that for me her clock is forbidden to strike any particular hour, I always say as I enter her room and honour her with my welcoming kiss, "Goodness, look at the time—nine, and I have to meet Jones on business at ten." Perhaps I may remain with her till eleven or even later, but by saying that I have an appointment at ten I have built my bridge for an honourable retreat. It's true I may have to curse the phantom Jones as a difficult person whom I dare not offend. Indeed, I may even make my lady grow to hate the phantom Jones, but in doing so I console myself with the fact that I have behaved like a perfect gentleman by leaving her happy in the certainty that no one but Jones could have compelled me not to meet the milkman on his morning round. Incidentally also, I know that I have behaved extremely well to my best friend—myself, for I have not squandered some of the few precious hours left to me.

"Oh, no! to be thoroughly certain how to ear-mark your hours is by no means a sign of age.

# NIGHT LIGHTS

" The telephone and rapid transit have destroyed the art of letter-writing, and while to-day there are no Lord Chesterfields, and we hope not any of his sons, the catching of the word on the wing and the flinging of it back to the assembled company is one of the great pleasures which all of us, and especially the debility and gentry, should be encouraged to cultivate.

" As a man who has lived every moment of his life and has drunk deep of pain and pleasure, I can say without hesitation that the hours I have spent listening to the talk of men and women whom I have loved (and I think I have been more truly fond of men than women), are among my most precious remembrances. A kiss is forgotten but an epigram is for all time—information gained is a gilt-edged security—but flashing eyes and parted lips are only the very doubtful shares of Life's stock exchange. And, therefore, my dear Edward, be joyful rather than grieved at this change which has occurred in your outlook on life.

" Whether talk in itself is brilliant or appears so as it rises to the surface with the bubbles of good wine is not the point. Even light-hearted talk is wonderful, for the merry chatter of the night is a symphony of friendship, a nocturne of happy companionship. It is by their " talk " that the loved ones who have gone are remembered, and it is the conversation of those who live which makes us long to see them again as soon as possible.

" What matters the handsome face, the elegant figure, the riches or the exquisite clothes of the diner, if his humour be of the mausoleum and his tongue not steeped in mirth-provoking acid.

" Give me the man or woman who can hand me a laugh, kindly or cruel, and gild with a jest the serious problems which

8

beset us all, and I care not if he is from jail or she is just going to it. I am their thankful friend.

"I always think that good talk should be pleaded in court as extenuating circumstances for all but the deadly sins, while the platitudinous bore should be given a life sentence for the most venal offence. I am sure you'll agree with me if you come to consider how short our stay is here, that talk is nine-tenths of life.

"It need not, of necessity, be particularly clever talk so long as it is happy talk, falling, as it must do, from the lips of the never possible to over-praise Micawbers of the universe. The man who does not cultivate this art and so contribute to the lightening of his friends' worries is one who deserves very handsome wreaths at an early funeral.

"The sun may shine brightly in a social heaven, but the droning of facts obscures its golden possibilities. What is the song of the birds in the wood but happy talk. That is why we listen and stand still enthralled. We think they sing. Not so. They have learned to talk beautifully. The thrush questions and the lark replies, but would he if the thrush were dull?

"Would the roses which surround the garden path we tread be just as lovely every season if their neighbouring dahlias did not nod approval, saying pretty things about their hips and petals.

"Listen to the gentle lowing of the herds, the welcoming bark of household pets, the call of pheasants and the purring of the wild. What is all this but happy talk? So why should we deny ourselves such pleasure?"

"My dear Alf," said Edward, "doubtless all you say is perfectly correct, but as to what are the greatest pleasures in life is not what I am bothering about. My difficulty is that at the age of fifty I find myself, although no doubt able to distinguish a Rembrandt from a Whistler, not at all sure whether the great Dutchman did not do most of his best work in Venice, or whether Marie Antoinette was not the divorced wife of Balzac and lived with Voltaire during Frederick the Great's transition period from æsthetic to Empire builder. What makes me so unhappy is that I have only had time to glean things superficially."

"I shouldn't take it too much to heart if I were you," replied Alf. "Mind you, my dear Edward, I am not saying that you are as ignorant as you pretend to be, but to have only a smattering of the world's literary treasures in middle life is something to be rather proud of—a thing to be envied. Think what a colossal literary and artistic fortune you have saved up to pore over as you sit on a milestone with sixty-odd carved on its base. The other fellow who has read hard and is disgustingly knowledgeable has little to look forward to at forty. Comfort yourself with this reflection."

"Perhaps you're right, Alf," said the doubting Edward, "but supposing you shake hands with double pneumonia or meet a profiteer with a new motor-car who decides you have no right to cross the road before you reach the age that good brandy has attained—what then?"

"Well, then, dear fellow, you will go to your grave wondering, as the maiden lady remarked to her married sister, and commence a literary career in a kingdom where thirsty sinners are compelled to drink split infinitives from goblets of asbestos."

Alf stopped talking, for suddenly the dancers had left the floor and had made for their tables to imbibe in haste and perspire at leisure. It was not altogether their damp departure that struck him so forcibly as a doubt which flashed across his dinner-laden brain as to whether he was drunk or dreaming, for in the distance the floor appeared to him to be rising.

# TWO MEN TALK

" Edward," he gasped, " am I wrong in supposing that the parquet over there is getting slightly above its station?" "It's moving," said Edward, " if that's what you mean. Its rise and fall is generally the best part of the coming cabaret."

Alf looked into the empty bottom of his many times filled glass and was much relieved. Sure enough, Edward had spoken rightly, for a young lady with impractically nothing on, followed by three swarthy, muscular young men, with clothing for which even the most expensive tailor could not have charged them more than half-a-crown, pirouetted on the stage which had so proudly reared itself on high for the occasion.

Of the diners, those of the West End pretended to look bored, but through half-closed eyes made inquisitive mental notes, while Suburbia, though appearing to be slightly shocked, was delighted, the men of outer London anxious their ladies should think that beneath their dress clothes they possessed as perfect figures as the naked stalwarts, while the village maidens hoped that their cavaliers would be certain that their bodices covered all the beauty which the female acrobatic dancer felt it was quite unnecessary for her to conceal. Shy smiles and timid glances made both sexes certain that unspoken questions had been answered silently in the affirmative.

Of course, they were all perfectly aware of the fact that next summer at Margate their bathing costumes would, as they always do, tell the varnished truth, still they gambled that the time which would elapse might obliterate the memory of to-night's perfection, and that love stepping into the water with them would gild the charms of each very imperfect male and female lily.

The cabaret performance was dull but daring in every way, the lady in the nude being flung rapidly from one

11

stalwart to the other as if she were something none of them were particularly anxious to be on intimate terms with for more than five seconds by the clock. As she was caught in mid-air no part of her anatomy seemed unknown to all of them, and this made Alf wonder, when a waiter told him that one of her three partners being her husband, under what circumstances, however compromising, it would be possible for him to be jealous of his two gentlemen partners.

He put this question to Edward who, looking a little surprised, ventured that although the art of terpsichore uncovered a multitude of skins, the probably unholy desires of the indolent unlooker could never enter the heads of those who danced for money's sake.

At a neighbouring table an American lady, who had overheard the remark, rasped : " Oh yeah ! "

Edward looked in her direction and was sorry to think that it had become the fashion to hear all that was flowery of the Bowery fall from the lips of beautiful American women, for she was, as Edward said, like all American ladies, terribly attractive, being dressed more for the South Sea Islands than the Arctic.

" She has a pretty back," he thought aloud, " a pretty front, in fact, a pretty everything. Don't you think so, Alf ? "

" Obviously, dear fellow," said Stanislaus, turning to look critically at Madame Oh Yeah ! " but frankly I am old-fashioned and dislike this present-day Lapsus Lingerie. I would rather some of her charms were hidden, dear Edward, for then I could let my thoughts run riot at pleasure, and give her the benefit of any imaginative doubt."

Looking to the right and left at the women at the near-by tables, Edward began to wonder if the beauties of the early Victorian era were really so different from those who fell beneath his roving eye, or whether it was their clothes that made them appear so, and put the question to his friend.

"Clothes, my dear Edward," replied Alf, "have no doubt a great deal to do with it, but not everything. We live in the days of Hamlet's dissolving flesh. Victoria was of the curves. We have to be content with the angles. This, I may say, for men being by no means a fair exchange. For while to-day nearly every married man discovers that he is sleeping with only half a woman, in the seventies a bridegroom was in grave doubt as to whether he was not reposing with two. Of course, whether one prefers quality or quantity is a thing that every man must decide for himself. Personally, I long ago made up my mind that halfpenny buns should only be served on one of the latter days in Lent and not encouraged as a sitting dish for the rest of the year. Adam, we know, was generous with one rib, but this is no reason to applaud the modern young lady for being over generous with her seven or eight aside. The slimness of the confidence trickster has become the cult of the *ingénue*. She dies to eat, but she lives to slim, and so she has encouraged the inventors of the pineapple and straw diet to go into partnership with the male milliner. Ah, no! it is not only the clothes they have taken off that makes them look so different ; it is the lack of avoirdupois and the double exposure that has added a problem to Euclid's infernal fifth book. However, thank Heaven, my dear fellow," he continued, " all women are not able to fight nature, you must never forget that Shakespeare knew this, for if you remember he wrote of them : 'There is a divinity that shapes their ends, massage them how they may.' "

Following the display of Eve and her three Adams, a female contortionist disported herself as well undressed as her predecessor, and contrived to place her body in such abnormal positions that Alf said, " If I were introduced to her at this moment I should have grave doubts which was her face," while Edward agreed that though her ladyship did seem to put her hands where her heart could never be, still she might possibly be the respectable mother of several children, and in the day time walk quite normally down side down as she carried a string bag full of vegetables in the Old Kent Road.

Some of the young ladies at Suburbia's table, having now got almost on speaking terms with nature, remarked that they could do " some of that which she was doing," and it was reported next morning that several *passée* wives without a past, having attempted in their bedrooms to emulate their jointless restaurant sister, had so injured their spines that they were placed for three months in the plaster called after a French city, much to the relief of their devoted husbands.

The cabaret over, the floor sank, blushing slightly, and the middle classes, the real backbone of England, having seen what they had seen, proceeded to dance with more abandon, feeling no doubt that they had grown to know something more definite about each other's concealed make-up.

" Who do you suppose all these people are, Alf, that one sees night after night gyrating with such dull faces and such gay behinds ? "

" I don't know, thank God," said Alf, as he puffed his five-shilling cigar which had cost the management at least two and sixpence. " I can only imagine they are quite good sorts who have come here to enjoy themselves from there and nowhere."

" They look it," said Edward.

# TWO MEN TALK

" They're not the usual old pre-war crowd," blinked Alf.
" They have the joy of Hampstead Heath written all over
them. They wouldn't even know how to spell *blasé*. Haven't
you watched them at dinner ? To begin with, not five per
cent. of them order their food before sitting down—a sure
sign of simple souls on " an occasion."

" It is only Suburbia, my dear Edward, which insists on
having its money's worth and prescribes that each of its
members must have a menu from which to choose its dishes
and study it as if they were picking losers at Epsom. This,
you see, not only creates for them amusing talk but enables
the dasher of the party who has been up West before to
explain that *moules mariniéres* are not too safe a dish because
the last time he ate them he had —— and then leaves it at
that. Here the young men of the party cough nervously
at the self-imposed pause, while the young ladies, looking
down demurely, try to convey that they are quite unable to
imagine what *moules* or any other unsafe edible could do to
a human being. Then again as the merits of various, to them
unknown, delicacies are discussed, the giggling is long and
loud as the wit of the party assures all present that ' an angel
on horseback ' is not Lady Godiva, notwithstanding the
fact that if he saw his lady companions in Richmond Park
mounted on half-a-crown an hour hacks he would have no
difficulty in finding a name for them as long as they kept their
seats. ' How bold Mr. Weston is,' thinks Miss Easton, ' to
speak of " our seats " without even the flicker of an eyelid.
But then,' she mused, ' he is to be forgiven, for he has
travelled extensively and knows his Paris twice,' and so
envying the *savoir-unfaire* these once a year men of leisure
acquire, Miss Easton turns up her nose at the memory of
Bournemouth and Southend.

"Oh, yes! the aristocrats of Suburbia when out on their night have great fun, for after the meal has been ordered and the waiters have given them exactly what the waiters had decided to give them, they finish up with the only thing of their choosing—the ices.

"It is with the ices that tongues are loosened. What alcohol does for Bond Street, ices do for those who shop on Saturday at the local *bon marché*. This product of Italy puts potential Wimbledon Athletes on their mettle and every step learned at Smithoni's Dancing Academy is boldly tripped so that the West End shall marvel and envy."

"Your eye is the trained eye, Alf."

"My dear fellow, nothing should escape the scooping optic of the modern journalist; even his dead grandmother or yours is fair game. Look at those two over there, for instance."

"The ones not speaking?"

"Yes, obviously married."

"And the pair to the right—are they married, Alf?"

"Certainly not. He is smiling at her as he orders."

"Yes, that never struck me before. How do you know these things, Sherlock?"

"Deduction, my dear Watson. It's very simple. Everything is obtained by deduction. For instance, if you see a good-looking woman walk into a restaurant with her cavalier laughing at her silly sallies, you can be sure he is hoping for the best worst, but when a lady of many charms is followed by a saunterer you can gamble that he is paying her rent and is anxious that the world should be made aware of the fact. Do you know I should consider myself extremely stupid if I couldn't tell the relations which exist between a man and a woman by the way in which he helps her on with her cloak."

"How?" said Edward, amazed.

"My child," winked Alf, "if he is a hunter the cloak is an excuse for touching her shoulder. If he has sent her head to be 'set up' he lets the once very helpful garment fall into its place as best it may. Am I right, Watson?"

"Always, Sherlock."

At this unqualified praise Alf became more of a man about town than ever. "Of all the types, Edward," he smiled, "nothing gives me more amusement to watch than the technique of the really clever 'bird of passage'—she who has perfected the art of loving not well but too widely.

"Her indifference to her elderly admirer is absolutely different to the encouragement she gives to the rosy-faced young man with money, who if he hadn't any wouldn't be with her.

"To the former she knows that his dying fires are to be fanned into flame by the cheque he will be grateful to give her. To this product who has earned his blood pressure her disdain is flattery. And when she ceases to be scornful and looks sad and mournful as the caviare—what a conquest has age made as it induces her through a sympathetic knowledge of the world to confide to him her manufactured sorrows—'things she has never told to any other living soul.' To the youth she is the 'girl woman' who has at last met some one who 'how can she say it?—he wouldn't understand.' She doesn't believe in men—she doesn't deny that there was—yes, there was *one* man whom she trusted but—well, why talk about that—and yet there are times when it does a woman good to say what is in her heart to a man who perhaps does understand a little! A hand reaches out to hers. She is surprised and startled. 'Are all men alike?' she almost wails. Oh! and she had thought that he of all

men would—don't do that again, she begs—her well-assisted
eyebrows becoming suddenly vertical. 'What wonderful
friends we can be—this will spoil it all.' And on this timid
fluttering sentence, which is embroidered with a cocktail
tear, the torrent of the shy believer in all women is let loose
as she knew it would be. She has given the same cue so
correctly on many occasions. It is the one the amateur never
fails to pick up.

"Ah! These heart-gangsters are the real artists to
watch at work, my dear Edward; anglers as adept with the
fly as they are with the lure, and who, having brought their
fish to her bank, return to the arms of their own particular
gigolo who believes the lady who keeps him, when she gives
the time-honoured description of her elderly friend as 'What!
that old boob? Do you suppose for one moment I'd
allow him to attempt even to kiss me? Darling, are you
crazy?' and of the boy, 'What! You're annoyed about
little Gilbert? Why? He's a baby—a generous big-hearted
baby who gives me things because I remind him of his
sister who died last year!'

"And so for the time being they are all happy, but the
end of the play is always the same. The old beau increases
his overdraft, the stupid boy breaks for a month his dis-
illusioned heart, the contented gigolo sings his wily way
towards the gates of the nearest gaol, and the lady, unless she
is more than ordinarily lucky, ultimately sinks, not too
gracefully, into a by no means velvet-lined gutter."

Having delivered himself of this word picture Alf sat back
looking like a Penny Flaubert filtered through Bloomsbury.

"Have you ever been taken in, Alf?" inquired Edward.

"Taken in?" said Alf, evidently very proud of the fact.
"Of course I have. What man hasn't. Taken in, yes, and

taken out and taken up the garden and down again. But it has never worried me. You see, I have always made a practice of gaining admittance to the boudoirs of beautiful ladies purely on my harm of manner." Remember, you never get hurt unless you allow yourself to become too serious, which of course is a thing no sane working man would ever think of doing. It is wise, my dear Edward, to always remember that ' brief love is here our portion.' If you are asked up on the twelfth to shoot grouse in the hope that you'll miss them, you don't expect to stay till the blackcock is on the wing with his plumage fit for a Highlander's bonnet. So why imagine that the invitations Cupid is generous enough to hand you should last any longer than the close time allowed for birds of another kind."

" I take it then you have never been upset when you found a woman untrue to you," said Edward.

" Do I look like that ? " said the undefeated one, " of course I haven't. But, dear boy, let me correct you, never say a woman is untrue to you. Always say she is unfaithful to the other fellow, for you can be perfectly certain that she has never told him that you ever even existed for her."

" I wish I had had a book of the rules years ago," sighed Edward. " It would have saved me many a lonely and sleepless night and my income would not have been milked for the purchase of those gifts every gentleman feels it is his duty to give at times of parting."

A LITTLE LATER

The saxophones were now in full blast and this, together with the thought that his many departed presents would have done him so much more good if he had kept them to use

as approach shots on new greens, made Edward a trifle
fidgety.

"Let us wander on to your rooms, Alf. I can't stand
this alibi music. It's just din after dinner, that's all."

"Right you are," said Alf, and purely out of respect for
his banker the florid one signed the bill.

"Do you know, I should like to kill the man who first
thought of music at meals," snapped Edward, as he quite
unconsciously flicked his cigarette ash into his companion's
coffee, who, not noticing the little attention, drank it thinking
it more than usually excellent.

"You would be wrong. There was a good deal of method
in that nobleman's gladness," gulped Alf. "First of all he
knew that music and dancing help the diners in many ways.
It's true a band may silence the wit, but it also makes that
dreadful hound, the professional story-teller, dumb. Think,
too, what an aid music is to illicit love-making. No elderly
husband can possibly object to the good-looking young man
his wife has invited to dinner taking her from the tangle at
the table to the tango on the floor. The band has bidden
them leave the semi-domestic mahogany and so out of earshot
the appointment they could never have made had they
remained seated, is arranged in perfect safety. Their departure
has also relieved love's congestion at the table itself, for
in the absence of those who have left to flirt with infidelity
the apparently correct spouse very probably reads a sonnet
in the eyes of his wife's best girl friend.

"Then, again, never forget, dear Edward, that the drum
is the enemy of the listening waiter. Oh! believe me, the
would-be fashionable world owes an enormous debt of
gratitude to the Dago who took such pains to make the night
go. How carefully he must have studied the heavy foot work

under the table which were the only messages Victorian lovers were able to send each other at feeding time. And how well he understood that not only were these pressing telegrams extremely unsatisfactory, but sometimes highly dangerous, being delivered as they often were to the wrong address.

"Think, Edward, could anything be more devastatingly embarrassing for an eager Galahad, who supposes his dress shoes to be doing really good work with the passionate brunette opposite him, than to hear her elderly chaperone say: 'Someone is on my foot,' or worse still, if the lady of really certain years looks up coyly from her fish straight into his eyes and accepts his pedal tribute as meant for her autumnal charms.

"Imagine, too, if it were not for dancing before, during, and after meals, what chance would the homeless bachelor, whose only eating guest is himself, have of making new women friends. Past him whirl many an ill-assorted couple. Over the shoulder of some dull rich gentleman he sees two wonderful orbs. They say to him, as they pass for the first time, 'You interest me, and you are alone.' As they flash by again they tell him their owner is delighted he thinks her attractive. Later, she half smiles and he doesn't, but the look he gives her says 'There's nothing I wouldn't do to amuse you. You think I am an expert in love. I am. I want you, and you want me. We must meet outside quickly.' And a few minutes later she is in the vestibule presumably telephoning, and he is whispering in her ear 'I am crazy about you.' Had it not been for music, how could she have danced to his flat the next evening at five, and two days afterwards have introduced him to her ponderous steady dinner ticket as a relation—not by marriage. So you see, Edward, if terpsichore and the Pipes of Pan were taboo, the modern menu would begin with dishes for dished diners, and end with Cupid sitting badly had on toast.

"Oh yes, though I don't dance myself, I am all for it; without it how could the imperfect lover be introduced— as he is to-day—to the ribs or rolls of the perfect beauty, who has set out to let imagination lead to that dangerous corner which boasts no Belisha Beacon."

As Dammit and Pithy Ass—this being the names the two friends were called by the many who disliked them— rose to leave, and wended their way through a maze of chairs, bald heads and heavy scents, Alf bade good night to a faded blonde who had obviously just had her face lifted, and whose jewellery very probably would have the same experience if Alf was any judge of her sleek wasp-waisted and well-paid dancing partner, while Edward nodded dis- tantly to a powerfully-built athlete whose only overseas exploit during the Great War was to have, as a wag put it, twice taken "female tanks" to Paris.

Having collected their hats they quite unconsciously lingered at the door of the ladies' cloak-room, and if not edified were interested to note the delightful nonchalance of the maids and matrons who entered its portals, and shortly returned through them to dance again. It made them realize for the first time that the winning of the War had, if it had done nothing else, given a certain careless poise to the women of England.

As they strolled into the Strand, Edward couldn't help noticing that Alf's hat was much the worse for wear, and said so. "Why don't you get a new one?" he asked. "In these hard times, no. It's quite good enough for me. I prefer to keep in my pocket the two sovereigns it would cost," said Alf, economically.

"Do you?" laughed Edward. "Have you ever stopped to think that you lunch and dine at a restaurant at least six times a week—a dozen times in all, and that you give a shilling on each occasion to the man who takes care of that awful thing on your head? That is, roughly, £30 a year, so that if you always go to the same restaurant, the gentleman who takes it from you can buy fifteen new hats, if he likes, while you go about looking like a decayed bookmaker."

"I've never seen one," said Alf.

"Drive slowly," said Edward to the taximan. "I hate going fast."

"That's no good," said Alf. "If you don't want a non-stop run into the hospital, my dear fellow, the only way to get him to drive carefully is to say 'Go easy; I drink very hard.' As you are not a woman, you can't say you are in an interesting condition, which is the formula, I believe, adopted by nervous ladies, even when the years have informed them that they might be slightly overstating the case. So be sure to say the next worse thing, which is that 'you drink like a fish.' Not only will this earn you a friendly smile, but an 'Orlright, guv'nor—I'm in the club, too,' which, by the way, is a little disconcerting if you have become acquainted with some of the new members at your own pot-house, for most of them—though they have to be seen—should never be heard."

As the taxi crawled down Piccadilly towards Clarges Street, Alf told Edward that he had been cut stone dead that day by a famous furniture dealer who, on being elevated to the Peerage, had informed all and sundry that he was unable to decide what title he should take.

"Surely," said Edward, "that's not your fault?"

"No, I know; but some one repeated the one I suggested."

"What was it?"

"Barren Bedstead," replied Alf; "which I thought wasn't too bad as the prosperous nobleman had no children, and had some time previously celebrated his golden wedding."

On arrival at Alf's flat Edward felt he was only five minutes ahead of a fit when, on tipping the Flag manipulator, he heard him grunt "Thank you."

Alf was about to open the front door when a young and very pretty girl stopped for a moment, and looked enquiringly at Edward. It was not the ordinary female glance of that time of night, which is generally "You're not going home so early, duckie, are you?" or something of that kind. It was the mute appeal one sees in the eyes of a stray dog.

"Hulloa!" said Alf to the girl. "What's the matter? You're crying. Anything wrong?"

"No, sir," she replied. "I want to get to Grays Inn Road, that's all; and I don't know what to do. I seem to have come wrong. Could you direct me?"

"Grays Inn Road?" said Edward. "You're walking away from it."

"I thought I was, sir," said the poor thing, tearfully. "Could you tell me how to get a 'bus from here?"

"Well, I don't know much about 'buses," bleated Edward. "Are you a stranger to London?"

"Yes, sir," said the girl. "I only came up yesterday to try for a situation which I hope to get to-morrow, and I've lost my way. London is so vast, and—and——" And then she burst out crying.

"Poor little devil!" whispered Alf. "Here, would you like a sandwich and a drink," he said, looking at the forlorn figure at his side.

"Thank you, sir. I won't have anything to drink, but if you could give me a biscuit I should be grateful. I've had nothing to eat since the morning."

"Well, of course," said Alf. "Come in!"

"No, sir, thank you. I'd rather not," said the girl, timidly. "But if you wouldn't mind handing me one on the stairs, it would be very kind of you."

"For heaven's sake, are you afraid?" asked Edward. "Do we look like people who would do you any harm?"

"Oh, no, sir! Please don't be offended. I didn't want to give any trouble; that was all."

After a good deal of persuasion the girl came up the one flight of stairs to the door of Alf's flat, and entering shyly seemed pleased to warm herself at the fire. She looked about her as if bewildered at her surroundings, and the unexpected kindness she had met with.

Sandwiches were produced, and though she refused a whisky and soda, never having tasted one in her life, she consented—after a lot of pressing—to accept a glass of port as she was cold, and looked it, poor soul.

Her story was a simple one, and she told it in a halting kind of way. She had lost her father in the second battle of Ypres, was one of five, and her mother was an invalid; but she didn't wish to complain. She was glad to have found work so that she would be able to help those at home.

Both Edward and Alf were very touched, and Alf ever generous with the money he had borrowed from Edward, said: "Look here! I hope you won't mind my giving you this—it's only a trifle—a couple of pounds. Please take it. I shan't miss it, and it may do you a bit of good, and anyhow, you'll be able to take a taxi and drive straight home. At this time of night a little girl like you ought not to be in the streets. You'll probably be insulted—you know what I mean, and so do accept it, will you, to please me ? "

It took both Alf and Edward quite a long time to get the poor child to put the money into her cheap little purse, and she left too overcome to do anything but blurt out her somewhat incoherent thanks as she went downstairs, turning halfway to smile at her benefactors.

The front door banged behind her, and the two men settled themselves in their arm-chairs a trifle more comfortably than usual feeling that they had done something for some one who really deserved it.

" I'm glad you gave her some of my money, Alf," said Edward.

" So am I," said Alf. " Poor thing, she looked pretty worried, didn't she ? "

" Yes," said Edward, " she did. It's a mighty hard world for some people. I'm jolly glad we helped her on her way."

" Rather ! " said Alf.

It was not till the next morning that Alf's valet reported the loss of three silver spoons and a gold cigarette case.

### THE SAME NIGHT

Alf's abode was like the apartments of a hundred other bachelors. It lacked the touch of a woman's hand, but not the imprint of her feet, as had the carpets been gramophone records they would have been adorned by a picture of Alf looking a perfect dog, listening at a loud speaker beneath which would surely have been printed " His *Mistress's* Voice."

# TWO MEN TALK

The untidiness of the room, although not a beautiful dis-order which, of course, is an *un effet de l'art*, was rather jolly, as it created an atmosphere without which the many delightful things to be seen on all sides might have been thought to be the property of some " precious person," which was the last thing even Alf's worst enemy would have accused him of being.

As if to leave no doubt that the sitting-room was one in which a " he man " worked and idled, Alf's servant rather encouraged a confusion which permitted a priceless twelve-inch bust of Marie Antoinette to support two or three much-used pipes, while the Bluthner more often than not was the resting place of the tantalus and the syphons.

" Have you ever noticed," said Edward, as they chatted away unceasing, " that you and I talk on every conceivable subject, and that we never reach finality about any of them ? "

" Of course we don't. Why should we ? If we did, there would be nothing left to discuss," laughed Alf.

" Besides, what do we talk about, as a rule—women mostly, and everything connected with them. Well, there is certainly nothing approaching finality about the worrying —though necessary—creatures they are, is there ? As the caged squirrel never tires of his wheel, so men between the the hours of eleven and one in the morning, seldom cease to drivel about Love, Religion, Politics and War, or a dozen other subjects on which they know it would be indecent to agree."

" I can't understand, Alf," said Edward, as they sat talking far into the night, " how is it you have never been unhappy on discovering you had been let down by a lady."

" Can't you ? My boy," grinned Alf, " you would if you

had learned early in life that it is only the optimistic pessimist who thinks he needs no breast-plate or paldrons to save his heart from the javelins the opposite sex are preparing for him almost in the first hour of their rhapsody, for, believe me, even a thin woman is too fat to be seen through."

" Surely they are not all like that, Alf ? "

" Ninety-five per cent. of them are," replied the writer of leaders. " And why shouldn't they be ? Unless they are embarking on what they hope will be a happy marriage, their instinct demands that they should prepare for early retreat at the first sound of battle, whether it be the conflict which spells disillusionment, fear, boredom, or the sight of fairer pastures which they have been able to gain a glimpse of from the mountain heights of love to which we have led them.

" And please realize, dear fellow, they are not to be blamed. We should never grumble at what *might* have been. We should always be grateful for what *has* been—the past was ours—so we must be generous and let the future be theirs.

" If your lady is very much younger than you are, be certain that long before she has allowed you to take her in your arms she has weighed up the situation extremely carefully. Don't you believe that at any time you have ever swept even the most inexperienced of them off their feet, and that a sudden impulse on their part is the reward of your extraordinary attraction.

" Oh, dear no ! If, as I say, she is still young, she will ask herself, as nearly all women do—mind you, in some cases perhaps subconsciously—' Is this good enough ? ' and if she becomes yours, she will have agreed with her conscience that it is.

"It may be that at first she thinks you are wonderful—and this ridiculous conclusion on her part having been arrived at—her desire for you is your ally. On the other hand, it may be that your help, or your money, make it worth her while to decide that valour is the better part of discretion; but, believe me, a woman's acid test of pleasant adventure is one and one only—'Is it good enough?'

"The sophisticated single lady hooks you, as it were, to fit in with her other fixtures, while the length of your *amour* with a married charmer depends impurely on how inquisitive, stupid or accommodating her husband happens to be.

"Knowing this, the modern Casanova should always be prepared for an air raid during an adventure."

"This means, then, Alf, that you have loved all your life with your head and not your heart."

"But, of course, dear fellow. A man's heart is for the *one* woman if he is fortunate enough to meet her. You can take it from me that she won't care twopence about his head and all the feminine problems with which it is crowded, but his HEART—ah! if she possesses that, she has won what no other woman has ever even caught a glimpse of, and she will be happy and content, for the wiseacres may say what they like—men only really love once. The roosts may have been many, but the builded nest is for all time."

"You are no doubt quite wise, Alf, in having insured yourself against hurt, but absurd as you may think me, I'd like to bet you've never known the happiness I have. You have never understood the terror of loss, the agony of jealousy, the hopes, the doubts, the longings and the anxiousness of uncertainty—all of which have more than often been backgrounds for great joy.

"You have been content to believe in no one—but because I have believed in all, I have had greater moments in a thousand ways than you have. We have both lost— you in smiles, I in tears—but at least I have gained more by writing 'For ever' than you have in scribbling 'For never.'

"Besides, you have no memories, while I—believing implicitly that the women who have left me—suffered as I did, love them still even after years, as good friends ; while you, have only the consolation of saying 'I am alone ; but oh ! how clever I've been.' Oh no, Alf ! I wouldn't alter my rules in the game of Love for yours. All women to me are beautiful and adorable things, and I am content to let them take back what they have been divine enough to give— or, if you like it better—to have loaned me."

"I don't say you're wrong, dear Edward, any more than you may feel I am not right. We are chess players who approach our adversaries from different angles—that's all. You are brave enough to open your game with a bandage over your eyes. I prefer to know exactly what my queens are doing. Who can say which is the wiser—he who trusts or he who believes in nothing ? "

"That I don't know," said Edward, "but I do know which is the happier."

"All the time ? " asked Alf.

"No, but on balance," answered Edward.

"Maybe ! " said Alf.

The hours ticked away, every conceivable ordinary topic was lightly touched upon, but, as usual, they proved only to be the embroidery preceding the main topic which every man who is really a man, desires to discuss—" Woman "— and Edward found himself harking back to Alf's profound dissertation on the female sex a few hours previously, indignant that his friend, without, of course, mentioning names, was sceptical about all the ladies who had honoured them with their friendships.

"Do you mean to say, my dear Edward, that you've never been turned down by the adored ones of your days and nights?"

"I don't think so," came the reply. "It's true we have parted, but there has always been some really good reason why they have had to break things off."

"My dear simpleton," said Alf, "ninety-five times out of a hundred there is only one reason, *they have tired of you.*"

"Tired of me?" flashed Edward.

"Why, of course," replied the certain Alf. "So long as they annoy us by indulging in real love—there isn't a woman breathing who waves her heart good-bye. Women are the truest untrue things in the world, but when they leave us it's a change they need—that's all. They have grown accustomed to our smile; our jokes are engraved for them on stone, and our laughter, which was once music, has become an echo. It's true that another man's wife who has sought adventure in your rooms may love you and leave you through fear of detection, but this is rare, for most of the married ladies of one's acquaintance are worthy of V.C.s for their reckless-ness when—how shall I put it—they elect to go over the top as *Vivandières* in Colonel Cupid's Emergency Corps.

"No, dear fellow, I'm sorry to disillusion you, but be sure when you were left by your lady, this happened because you had ceased to please her. The furrow on your brow shows me you are doing rapid and painful thinking. Three faces in particular, perhaps, at this moment are looking at you from a pillow or this table-cloth.

" The brunette ? You can't believe it ! She had cried salt tears the morning she kissed you *au revoir*, for the last night had been the most passionate of any. Had she not whispered in the darkness that there had never been anyone else but you—and never as long as she lived could there ever be another. And had you not, brimming over with delight at her avowal and happy in your security, pitied her when she wrote a few hours later of her abject misery that she could never see you again because of her thought of *your* future.

" How you suffered for all she was going through. You knew is was her mother's fault, not her's—didn't you ? You were willing to blast your career—you begged her to blast it—but she, noble creature that she was—refused to see you for fear she might be weak and give in to you and then she could never attempt to be strong again. Isn't that what the brunette said ? "

" I think it was," said Edward, looking a little sheepish.

" And don't you know what really happened, my lad ? She had considered the whole position carefully. There was more money elsewhere or some one younger—or some one had appeared who attracted her even more than you did at your first meeting. You can't conceive it possible, can you, that in the darkness which once had been all yours, she could murmur everything she had said to you to another, or that she had turned that pink-shaded light near that charming couch of her's up higher so as to look into another's eyes ? But is was so.

" Your vanity let her off easily. I do hope I'm not destroying charming illusions. And why should you blame her ? She had given you much and was probably as true to you as you were false to her during many a month. The balance of unfaithfulness should always be to a man's credit, while his lady is really his—but always remember that when she closes love's account the debit side is invariably in her favour.

"We men generally open the ledger *d'amour* for bad, but women always have the privilege of closing it for good."

That night Edward, in his service flat, went to his couch troubled. He couldn't believe that Alf was right about the charming fickleness of women. The thought that he had ever been deceived was perfectly incredible.

In the darkness he saw a dozen beautiful ladies smiling down upon him, and as he lay staring up to where he knew the ceiling must be, he was certain beyond all doubt, poor fellow, that the divine creatures whose faces were fast fading one into the other had all been as true as steel.

At last he slept, a troubled, restless sleep, for he dreamed that no female had ever been true to anybody, and on waking he solemnly swore that he had finished with women and their wiles for ever.

The fog peeped prettily through the window, wishing him "bad morning."

There was a knock at the door. A maid he had never seen before placed the morning papers on his bed. She was tall and an extraordinary beautiful girl.

Some months later her gowns at Ascot were much admired.

It was on the night of a General Election that Alf and Edward found themselves in their favourite restaurant seated on a divan with their backs to the wall.

Alf financially always sat in this position—Edward only at intervals.

It had been a wonderful evening. Everyone who was

nobody had turned up to eat patriotically, and even those on a diet had ordered soup to watch Labour drop into it.

Never had there been such excitement since the evening papers some weeks previously had announced to a bewildered world that two married Hollywood stars had lived together happily for nearly six weeks.

It was a marvellous night. Even defeated candidates drank success so copiously to the new régime that solely for England's sake they fell with the pound sterling as they made unsteady exits in the small hours. Foreign waiters who had voted for the Socialists were all smiles, and did not hesitate to say how glad they were they had supported their Conservative member. Some of them, however, who understood English imperfectly, had voted for the " Communicists," as they called them, being under the impression that this party was some sort of religious organisation.

But, on the whole, with the exception of an old maiden lady, who had put a cross on her voting card against each of the candidates' names, wishing, as she said, to send a kiss to both of them, there was no doubt Britain had done its duty and with the help of Mrs. Pomery and Mr. Krug, was not backward in saying so.

Thirteen hundred people had sat down to dinner—thirteen hundred had risen, not perhaps with the same elasticity physically, but certainly with increased gaiety mentally.

It was a night on which strong men had held the hands of wives whose husbands were perfect strangers to them.

The Portuguese, the Argentines and the Greeks had sung *God Save the King* with gusto, Americans had toasted the War Debt, and there wasn't a Briton present who had not lifted his glass over and over again to the Commissioners of Income Tax.

# TWO MEN TALK

It was, indeed, an evening of " Hail fellow, well wet ! " with everyone.

The celebrities present, who adorned the most conspicuous places, and there were hundreds of them, very modestly did all they could to remain as much noticed as possible, and on every face shone the smile of " Alone I did it."

Alf and Edward, having grown weary of applauding the downfall of men who should never have left their empty soap-boxes in Hyde Park, and of cheering the return of those who probably were going to make life more unbearable by the imposition of every conceivable tariff, had spent a large part of their evening pointing out well-known people to each other and discussing the genius they wished the men possessed and the charms which the beauty parlour had failed to give the women.

The atmosphere of the restaurant was naturally political. Over it all was the voice of Vansittart, which breathed o'er Eden, while even the dinner menu had been designed to meet the occasion.

The Fish was Absolutely Chamberlain, the Entrée Exceedingly Duff Cooper, the Roast Decidedly Winston, and the Bird Belisha. The Tipsy cake had been re-named Bomb Astor, while Defeated Members *en brochette* showed that the management could be mildly humorous and not unmindful of the wishes of its patrons.

Round and about were to be seen the sons of great men who knew themselves to be so much bigger than their fathers, and here and there were many celebrated politicians, the majority of whom would have found great difficulty in earning three pounds a week in the open market.

Edward watched our rulers with great interest. Alf looked at them with a sceptical eye, wondering why they had ever been elected to misgovern our troubled land.

Perhaps their constituents felt they were right; and if so: "Well," thought Alf, "they have got all they deserved."

"Oh," he sighed, "what bores most politicians are."

"You think so?" said Edward.

"Yes," replied the man who knew, "they bore me to absolute extinction. Their shop is even more soul-killing than the pleasant lies of the fisherman or the dullness of the hunting man who usually, through a face which looks like nothing so much as a loud speaker painted vermilion, informs you either where 'they found' or how they ran for fifty minutes without a check (which is very like a theatrical venture financed by a syndicate), and then proceeds to explain at length the Song of Hounds and the distinguishing note of the puppy, which is the spit of his great-grandsire's.

"I remember a famous surgeon telling me once that only five per cent. of the men who passed out of hospital with honours were really first-class, and to my mind this is a very generous view if taken of politicians as amusing companions.

"The shop of the barrister, with its 'Quite—quite—I agree,' and his interminable recital of cited cases, the shop of the soldier with his sly stories of pretty little Mrs. Carruthers, whom he met in the Hills while her husband remained at Rumbellypore—in fact, all shop except that talked by the man who keeps one, and we are only pleased to meet him if we happen to have paid his bill, is a punishment which the greatest sinner does not deserve.

"But the gentlemen who are elected to what I believe for most of them is a sheep-pen, and who when they escape from it think aloud as Penny Pitts or Farthing Foxes, are sad affairs, for they do not confine themselves to small shop —they are co-operative.

# TWO MEN TALK

"Mind you, I admire the budding and blooming politicians enormously for their bravery in many directions. It must take no small amount of courage to gain votes by kissing spotted babies who dribble generously, and to hail as long-lost brothers alcoholic loafers who hold the destiny of our Empire in their hands—hands which have become horny through the continual toil of grasping the dole."

"Are you referring particularly to the old Parliamentary hands or the fledglings?" asked Edward.

"Not all of either sort, of course," said Alf. "Among the ancients one naturally meets a good percentage of great brains, and among the young men a light that for the time being is hiding itself under some lady's bustle. For the latter one cannot feel anything but profound pity, for they have given up happy village cricket to become members of a dull club.

"I don't remember ever having sat at a dinner table opposite a young man who has just got in for Wigdale, or some other tolerant constituency, that my neighbour has not pointed at him and whispered to me with bated breath: 'He is perfectly brilliant. Everyone in the House, not excepting the charwoman who sweeps up the platitudes on Sundays from the Members' Smoking Room, is convinced that some day he will be Prime Minister.' Let us forget them," said Alf, "there are quite a number of amusing people about to gape at."

This was true; on their left sat a bride of thirty-five who had gone off before she got off. Alf couldn't remember her face, although he knew her name, but informed Edward that he had admired her when she was a slim young thing of twenty. Now she was fourteen stone stripped for gym. "How nice for Jim," was Edward's facetious reply; to which Alf, with true British humour, said : " No, old boy, her husband's name is Charles."

" Who is that pretty youth," asked Edward, " who leans so idly against her pneumatic arm ? "

" Oh ! that fellow with the body of a colt and head of a filly ? He is one of Chelsea's latest ' finds.' Brilliant, I hear. Only twenty-six and writing his life."

" Really," said Edward. " Why doesn't he take it ? "

This was for Edward not a bad jest, and indeed Alf condescended to murmur that he wished he'd made it. Edward was not original enough to remember what Whistler said on a similar occasion to Wilde.

" Tell me," said Edward, looking a trifle critically at the young man he had suggested was eligible for the Suicide Club, and whose name he felt sure he would see some day in the Honours List as a Dame of the British Empire, " What do you make of him, Alf ? Pansy ? "

" Bi-sexual, I should imagine," replied Alf. " But then I find it difficult to understand this new degeneration. They have only succeeded in making me feel extremely uncomfortable when I go to Barrie's masterpiece and Peter Pan inquires so anxiously, ' Do you believe in fairies ? ' Though, mind you, I do think we owe a great deal to the person who invented the word ' pansy ' as applied to the young man of to-day of indefinite sex, for it is a pleasant word and one that may be used without offence in the home of early Victorian ladies who do not understand what it is intended to convey."

" I've often wondered," said Edward, " why the name pansy was given to foul youths who glide through life like petulant silk worms—the pansy is an extraordinarily pretty flower."

" Perhaps that's why," replied Alf, " or is it, do you

suppose, because the petals of a pansy look like a Skye terrier's face ? "

" Why insult any kind of dog, dear Alf, let alone a harmless terrier ? "

Not far away sat a famous society climber, Mrs. Edelwiss, now a widow. Alf pointed her out to Edward, remarking sagely that while all widows wear weeds, few wear well. She dripped diamonds and her ample figure poured generously over each side of her three sizes too small chair. Richer even than the poor—she looked more like the Bank of England than the Old Lady of Throgmorton Street herself.

" What a dreadful looking woman," said Edward. " She must be terribly well off to be able to order people with her food."

" She is," said Alf. " She's well enough off to pay what she will never owe."

" Fancy," said Edward. " Did her husband leave her much ?"

" As often as he could, I believe ! Her success in life has been due to the fact that she is a woman who would only take ' yes ' as an answer."

At a table in the distance they saw a recent hero of the Divorce Court, who, being a heavy sleeper with a nasty habit of dreaming, had got into trouble at home by forgetting to take the precaution of calling his mistress by his wife's Christian name. At his side brooded the fair co-respondent, draped in a wonderful fur cloak, which had been given her not so much to keep her warm, for this was unnecessary, but to keep her bright. A hard-faced nagging lady, thought Alf, who deserves a husband who eats biscuits in bed.

" It's funny, Alf, isn't it ? " said Edward, " how differently the words Mistress and *Maîtresse* fall on the ear, ' to put it poetic-like.' Mistress in English, to me, is supremely vulgar, the label of a lady which a maid has met at a registry office, and with whom she has concluded a bargain for services to be inadequately rendered. Whereas ' *Ma Maîtresse* ' conjures up visions of a charming hostess amidst beautiful surroundings, who, however long she has been your friend, only confers her favours upon you after a new and gallant wooing.

" That's where Mrs. Warren's French sisters are so clever. They keep other women's husbands true to them by never allowing the affairs of love to become a habit. Believe me, there would be far fewer divorces if every married woman nailed a knocker on her bedroom door."

" I expect you're right, but talking of mistress and *maîtresse*, it never struck me there could be so nice a distinction between French and English words. I wonder what Adam called Eve. I suppose as his knowledge of French was very limited the former must have been the name he gave his lady when he decided to go into the fruit business with her, and they set up shop under a lilac bush with the serpent as their first customer."

The room was full of the camera-men's selected, so full, indeed, that it was not until afterwards that Alf and Edward remembered how famous actors had congratulated each other on their failures, how Society beauties had admired each other's make-up in private life, how popular authors had praised the style and literary brilliance of their rivals' latest effort which they hoped they would never read, and how one *prima donna* had offered another her house for the season, fearing that living in a flat might affect her singing even more if possible than it had already.

Nearby, Edward's eye fell upon a tall, melancholy-looking individual, obviously boring a delightful lady, who had regret written across her face for having in a weak moment said something about " love, honour and obey."

" I bet you," said Edward, " you cannot add those two up."

" Oh, yes, I can ! " said Alf. " I happen to know them. The gentleman you refer to is extremely rich. This, of course, you will gather, dear fellow, from the fact that his wife is wearing a necklace composed of emeralds as big as the green pastilles we buy for our sore throats."

" Stockbroker ? " inquired Edward.

" Dear me, no," said Alf, " nothing so imaginative as that. He happens to be one of the largest carpet manufacturers in the world."

" Is he ? " said Edward, and after a moment's thought he made, what, for him, was by no means a bad jest. " Yes, he looks dull, but that's probably because he is wondering how he can supply a ' long felt want ' " ; and then added : " How is it, I wonder, that so many men with money have so little sense of humour ? "

" Ah," said Alf, " I long ago discovered that rich men are like dead men, they tell no tales."

" Do you know Coward, Alf," asked Edward, as he stared at this much discussed young man.

" Intimately," replied Alf.

" What sort of a fellow is he ? "

" One of the most delightful men I've ever met," answered the dusty pastel, " and the rarest of all birds—a genius, with most uncommon common sense. I know no one whose brains I admire so much with the exception of my own, of course, which, my dear Edward, you will agree, is the greatest praise one man can give another."

The two friends sat for several minutes watching Coward and Charles B. Cochran, his partner in many a triumph.

" A great combination," thought Alf aloud, "both in
their own way superlative. It always annoys me, Edward,
you know," said Alf, " to hear Cochran continually referred
to only as ' a great showman.' This, of course, he is, but
I do wish those who write of him would also label him a
great artist for his sense of all that is beautiful in the theatre
is unequalled on our stage to-day, and his love of quality
and knowledge of values in the actor unrivalled."

When the orchestra played *God Save the King*—which it
did at intervals throughout the evening—Coward, on hearing
it for the nineteenth time, turned to the showman of show-
men and asked him why they *would* keep on playing the
music from " Cavalcade," and incidentally wondered if they
ought not to receive Royalties on this tune, which he felt
in time might make quite a good National Anthem.

The two friends, hearing another result announced, began
to discuss the state, in fact, the almost awful state, of the
political parties.

" I suppose whichever side gets in," droned Edward,
" nothing very much will be done. The fate of the
Empire will, as is generally the case, remain in the lap of
the gods."

" Obviously," replied Alf; " I only hope the gods won't
open their legs and drop the Empire on the floor."

" Well, don't let us get serious, Alf. This new Government
which is being born to-night is quite enough for one evening,"
said Edward.

" Right," said Alf.

They took off their smoke-tinted glasses to stare at less
brilliant lights.

" I say," said Alf, " do you see that cove sitting under
the palm over there ? "

"I do," said the brainy Edward.

"Well, he's very rich and supposed to be the meanest man in London."

"Quite unforgivable, Alf. There is no excuse for every rich man not being a good and generous one, if he is not, he is a bad man."

"Still, many people are hard driven, and have to resort to dodge and subterfuge to skate on the thin ice of unstable finance, haven't they, old boy?"

"Naturally, look at us," winked Alfred. "But talking of dodges, I remember a clergyman who had a congregation so certain of their souls that they put little or nothing into his collection plate, and nearly shepherded him into the workhouse. It was his practice, being of a somewhat unimaginative turn of mind, to buy two sixpenny sermons every Saturday at the local bookseller's, for use on Sunday, one for the morning and one for the evening service. As time went on, and his parishioners grew more certain than ever they could enter Heaven without his help, it became a question with the poor padre as to whether it should be one sermon on Sunday and an egg for breakfast on week-days, or two sermons on Sunday, and only thoughts of the farmyard on the other six days. Sad, or one may say sensible to relate, the Gospel in its contest with his stomach was counted out in the sixth round. The egg won. The riddle he then asked himself was how he was to avoid being repetitious on the same day.

"He confided his fears to his cook-housekeeper, and in a flash she solved the problem for him. Knowing that he was the possessor of a very fine set of artificial teeth, she advised him to learn the one sermon by heart and preach it at the morning service with *his teeth in*, and at evensong to preach it again but with his teeth out.  This he did, and the compliments and thanks he received from those who listened to him in the evening made him extremely happy."

How fickle is fortune—how many a great invention the child of accident !

Seated in an alcove not far from their table, Alf caught sight of Sharkstein, the moneylender.  He seemed extremely happy and had all the appearance of a conger about to roam from its hole in search of prey.

" Greasy looking brute," said Edward, who had turned in the same direction as his friend.

" Yes," said Alf, " fat as a pig.  Rather like Cæsar about to become a mother.  In fact he's so fat that they say he can never believe he's sleeping alone."

" Why do you suppose he seems so pleased ? " inquired Edward.  " Surely he hasn't ' got in ' for anywhere, has he ? "

" My dear fellow," said the dusty one, " England will stand for a good deal, but not for Sharkstein.  He's delighted with life because he sees in everyone here who is a trifle tight a prospective client.  The deep and merry Christian voices he is listening to to-night he knows he is certain to hear against his wailing wall in Mayfair on the not far distant to-morrow.  A horrid specimen, my dear Edward, who feeds fat on the misfortunes of his fellow creatures.  He broke Algy Bellamy, but I'm happy to say Algy got one back on him by composing his hoped early-to-be-epitaph ; it ran :

HERE LIES (AS USUAL)

SAMUEL SHARKSTEIN

WHO DIED DEEPLY REGRETTED

BY ALL WHO DIDN'T KNOW HIM.

Alas !  Algy has departed and the shark remains.

" They do say he is preparing for his demise by drawing Bills on fireproof parchment."

" Very hot," said Edward.

" Yes, old boy. Oh, he'll go through it when Satan welcomes him home. The only drink he'll be given will be the watermark on the documents in his shroud, and, mind you, whatever he gets he'll deserve, for his attitude to his clients has always been ' Live and let die.' "

" I wonder if Hitler was right," murmured Edward.

" What, about that class? Of course he was," answered Alf. " For you must remember that the really nice Jews detest the usurers as much as the Christians do who are invited by them to the feast of the Golden Fleece. The Sharksteins should be strung up to the nearest lamp-post, for they all possess the fine feelings of a hungry crocodile, and there isn't one of them who for money wouldn't play clock golf round the Cenotaph."

" Who is the aristocratic looking gent with our friend, Alf? Am I right in supposing I have seen him act? "

" You are quite wrong, Edward. You have seen him on the stage, maybe, but by no means doing what you suggest."

" But surely he was a star once, wasn't he, Alf? "

" Yes, but not twice, as W. S. Gilbert remarked about an artist who had been very difficult in her prime."

" And yet," said Edward, gazing into the face of the man who had crept into the boudoir of many an ambitious *ingénue* on an unsigned contract; " he has been successful, hasn't he? "

" Oh, yes, you see sincere insincerity takes many a fellow quite a long way. Buy a smile, lean on an Austin Reed, say much, think little, wear a Guard's tie even though your father started life on the L.M.S., and you'll be surprised how you can slide from the giddy highbrow heights to the depths of financial stability. But really," said Alf after a pause, " why am I holding forth about so tiresome a person ? I don't know. Let us forget him."

" You are cruel, Alf," said Edward.

" Only to be unkind, old boy, believe me," answered the sixpenny oracle.

The band having played *God Save the King* for about the twentieth time, only the Armenians and Abyssinians present, neither of them by the way being as black as they are painted, stood up, and Alf, commenting on the splendid loyalty of those whose complexions could never be an advertisement for Elizabeth Arden, caught sight of that famous dramatist, Freddie Lonsdale, who was one of Edward's oldest and best friends.

The brilliant Freddie waved them the time of night and hurried on to a candidate he did not know to congratulate him on having lost his seat, and then returned with all the enthusiasm of the Portuguese army in retreat to rejoin the distinguished party with whom he had been all the evening.

" I wish I knew Lonsdale," said Alf. " It would be difficult," replied Edward. " I don't think he knows himself, but I should pick your hour if I were you when you *do* meet him for the first time. Your ' on ' day may very possibly be one of his ' offs ' when his toast at meals is ' Absent friends —long may they remain so.' Personally, we have known each other so many years that every day is the same with us. It is generally made up of a grouse or two, a laugh or two, half an epigram, a slight hymn of hate at things in general, and then ends up by him telling me the story of the fourth act of his new three-act play. I'm devoted to him."

" I always think he has the face of a Greek god and the ʿart of a low comedian," ventured Alf.

" There I can't quite agree with you," said Edward. " He

always looks to me like a miniature Voltaire when in repose, and Puck *in excelsis* when he is on the alert. If by any chance you meet him at a supper he has forgotten to give, you will find him one of the best companions in the world. He is always saying something you can go out and dine on. I remember last New Year's night begging him to wish a rather objectionable man with whom he had quarrelled ' a Happy New Year.' After a lot of persuasion the kaleidoscopic Freddie agreed to offer his enemy his hand. ' For your sake, dear Edward, I will go and wish him a Happy New Year, but, mind you, *only one.*' His wit is devastating. Somebody once said they would hate to be his enemy, to which a wag replied, ' It is worse to be his friend,' but remarks of this kind are only the happy banter of the small hours."

Not far from the table to which our famous dramatist had journeyed, sat another of London's landmarks—that swashbuckling musketeer, Hannen Swaffer.

Alf pointed him out to Edward as :

" The one with the melancholy visage who is smiling so good-naturedly at the world. He always seems to me to be a literary Solomon Eagle who should have been painted by Raeburn in his powder period. Look at him ! " almost shouted Alf, " He is surrounded by all the beauty and brains of theatre-land. You will notice they are in perfect agreement with everything he says and are gathering up the words of witty wisdom which fall from his stylographic tongue. He is a grand fellow, is Swaff."

" He must be—so many people hate him."

" I love his honesty," said Alf. " He says what he thinks and what he thinks ten times out of ten is absolutely correct. Of course, any man who would operate on the heart of his best friend if he felt it his duty to do so doesn't court popularity, but I'm glad he is so absolutely fearless, it lets in a breath of much needed fresh air to the house of humbug most of us are condemned to live in. He is witty all day—and nothing gives me such a thrill as to see him more amused at his own jokes than he can ever hope anyone else will be.

"Among some of his *mots* he certainly should be given full marks for his criticism of George Arliss as 'The Iron Duke.' He re-christened the film 'The Ironed-out Duke,' and added that he hoped the charming actor would star with Elizabeth Bergner in a film to be called 'Disguise Me Never,' or by himself in a new version of Carroll's immortal story and call it 'Arliss in Wonderland.' "

"I thought his performance of Wellington extraordinarily good," said Edward, "though I am bound to say I think he would have been much wiser had he chosen to play Nelson rather than the 'up Guards and at 'em' old gentleman of Apsley House."

"Wellington never told the Guards either to get up or go to bed, dear Edward, but talking of Waterloo, it is not generally known that Bruce Bairnsfather got his idea for that inimitable drawing, 'We are Living at a Farm,' through happening to catch sight of the well-known engraving of Blucher shaking hands with Wellington at La Haye-Santé. For my own part, in studying this artistic offering, I have always felt that the horses of these two great soldiers must have been trained by an ancestor of Bertram Mills, for while bodies lie within inches of them, the hoofs of the quadrupeds have most considerately missed a hundred upturned faces. It may be that the painter intended that the noble steeds should not finish those off whom Napoleon had been so considerate as only to wound."

## THE MEETING OF WELLINGTON AND BLUCHER
## AFTER WATERLOO
*From the Painting by David Maclise, R.A.*

## " WE ARE AT PRESENT STAYING AT A FARM."
(In this cartoon by Captain Bruce Bairnsfather, in 1915, the artist had in mind the ruined farmhouse at Waterloo.

# TWO MEN TALK

"It has always been an extraordinary thing to me, and will ever remain so," said Alf, "that no honour of any kind was ever bestowed on Bairnsfather for his perfectly wonderful contribution to the spirit uplift he gave the nation during the darkest hours of the war. In 'Old Bill' he invented 'an England laughing'; he was the military Tom Webster of that terrific death struggle. Beneath each tale of magnificent disaster and heroic defeat, his caricatures and captions cried aloud from the mouth of his old soldier, 'All's well.' The great public loved him and thanked him for the comfort he brought in times of doubt, but the compilers of text-books on the art of killing forgot that it was priceless humour as much as anything else that helped Britain to march on to victory.

"But to return to Hannen Swaffer," continued Alf. "I remember once sitting behind him at the first performance of an extremely bad play, which grew steadily worse as the night wore on. At the end of the second act, to enliven the proceedings, a coffin was brought on the stage. This being more than I could bear, I leaned across to the man whom Lord Northcliffe nicknamed 'the Poet' and said, 'Isn't this awful, Swaff.? Fancy bringing on a coffin.' 'I wish I was in it,' replied Swaff.

"He is a great journalist, and though it may be news to many, he is really a very kindly man and, what is better still, so great a humorist that he is impossible of purchase."

Edward said: "Alf, if you were an actor you would probably get a good notice if Swaff. heard you had said that."

"On the contrary," said Alf, "if I were an actor, praise of this kind would encourage the Poet to dip his pen in a double solution of comic vitriol."

Looking at Lord Castlerosse steering his way across the

room by the stars—theatre and Hennessey alike—Edward, who was one of his greatest fans, said, " Alf, who was it described him as the Elephant and Castlerosse ? "

" It is so witty," replied Alf, " that I am pretty certain he made it up himself."

The two friends watched this splendid Irishman oozing good nature from every pore (and he has quite a number of them) as he surveyed the scene, wondering no doubt how much if any of it was worthy of mention in the " Londoner's Log."

" Ah," said Alfred, looking at the second page of the *Sunday Express.* " There is a real Grand Seigneur, if you like, and if he were only a trifle more robust he might well be taken for one of the notable figures of the Regency. What a pity he could not have been persuaded to play Henry the Eighth—then we should have seen what a great gentleman Elizabeth's relation was."

" I wish he had," said the cinema-minded Edward. " It is extremely galling that a mighty English King should be conceived by many who appear in Holbein's doublet and hose to be either a pig going to a wedding or a local butcher disporting himself at a Covent Garden Ball.

" You must meet Valentine, Alf, and when you do you will have the privilege of knowing a marvellous companion, a staunch friend and, when he chooses, a magnificent emotional and descriptive writer.

" Do you know," continued Edward, " I remember telling one of our greatest stylists that I had read an article by Castlerosse on religion, and that I ventured to think V. C. ought to be given one for its beauty and depth of feeling. The man I addressed said : ' I am more than sure that some of Valentine's writing will live.' "

# TWO MEN TALK

"I am only a verbal carpenter," chipped in Alf, "but I agree absolutely with your concealed stylist. It is the duty of someone to urge his Lordship of Castlerosse to become the Pepys of our time, for as a two-bottle man he can laugh to scorn the two-button men who to-day get a rush of blood to their feet after one orangeade."

"It can hardly be because they are on journalistic business bent," thought Edward, "that so many dramatic critics are supping here on this particular evening," and the good companions wondered why they had foregathered in force as they watched several of the most distinguished of that much-to-be-pitied coterie who, five nights out of six, are condemned to death in the theatre by many young ladies and gentlemen, who ought never to be seen because they can't be heard.

One of the most celebrated disciples of Hazlitt, James Agate, was the life and soul of a little group of enthusiastic amateur politicians. He had earlier that evening been broadcasting on his favourite subject, "The Hundred Worst Plays," and having pleasantly torn to shreds even those he had previously recommended to the public, he was relaxing amidst a clatter of knives and forks, looking upon the people about him with the eye of a tolerant Nero, whose only regret was that he had no cornet to play while the Socialists were burning.

"What a wit is Agate," said Alf. "He is possessed of one of the quickest brains I have ever fallen in with. It is like a brilliantly polished cog-wheel with the ratchet off. It buzzes on and on until lost in amazement at epigram and play of words one wonders if he ever lets fall the windows of an exceptional soul."

"Alf, you knew plenty of the great dramatic critics of long

51

ago," said Edward. " Tell me, as a team, do you think those of to-day compare with them ? "

" Don't be silly, my bonny boy," said Alf. " Of course they do. Frankly, I consider them, if not so powerful through lack of space and the world sensations which hourly crowd the theatre out in our great dailies, as a whole beyond words better.

" To begin with, they are by no means so vindictive and personally abusive as they used to be in olden times, and are much more inclined to dismiss rather than condemn.

" As for their knowledge of the play and the players, to say nothing of the Theatre of the World, surely they know more and look out upon a wider dramatic horizon.

" You must know, dear Edward, and not be surprised when I tell you that certain critics in the old days were to be bought, if not always with money, in kind. To-day it is superfluous to remark such a condition does not exist.

" Now we are lucky to possess a most distinguished company of gentlemen, who write with enthusiasm of the theatre, a glorious enthusiasm which gives the playhouse life.

" Take, for instance, Agate over there, of whom we were just speaking—a marvellous, vital, devastating, a rejoicing-at-success, a tomahawking-of-failure critic, cruel at times, but to be forgiven over and over again for the witty way he sentences men and women to oblivion.

" Whom more should theatre people thank heaven for than St. John Ervine, as scathing as Agate may be if he is displeased or disappointed, but scrupulously fair and with an unrivalled knowledge of the Drama.

" Ivor Brown, too, an author, my dear Edward, of genius, and for a man who could ' pan ' with a sentence a whole production a very kindly gentleman, who prefers to be helpful to those on the rugged road he knows they have so often to travel.

"Then think of Charles Morgan, one of the most distinguished of living writers, whose works will assuredly live, and——"

"Oh, well, that's enough," said Edward. "I don't want the life history of all the Princes of Fleet Street. I'll take your word for it that they are wonderful, even though you, being a journalist, are naturally as biased as a set of bowls."

The dawn of a new day was at hand before the hundreds of befuddled political partisans overflowed into the Strand, wending their way, some to their own homes and others to establishments they had never seen before, and which a week afterwards they wished they had never seen at all. But Life was ever thus. There is little difference between alcohol and an anæsthetic. The man who takes either is sublimely unconscious as to who is operating upon him.

Alf and Edward, who had been able to collar a taxi, caught sight of George Robey standing marooned on a refuge apparently unable to attract the attention of the driver of a conveyance of any description. Alf knew him well and shouted out: "George, jump in here."

George did so and hardly had he banged the door of their germ incubator behind him before he said: "Alf, have you heard this one? I don't suppose you have, because I only heard it myself an hour ago. It's quite good. A man who was extremely drunk sat down on a broken tumbler and cut himself severely on that part of his anatomy where so many people keep their brains. He was in great pain and left the party he was at very hurriedly. On arriving home he staggered to his dressing-room, took off his clothes and anxiously surveyed the damage he had sustained in the looking-glass. His decision as to the best remedy for his injuries was quickly made, and getting a large piece of sticking-plaster he hastened to cut it into strips to place upon the injured part. Having done so he went contentedly to bed. The next morning his wife said : ' You were very late last night, weren't you, Charles ? ' ' I was, I'm afraid,' said the somewhat sheepish Charles. ' And,' continued the wife, ' if I am not mistaken you were somewhat inebriated, my dear.'

" ' Why do you say that, sweetheart ? ' inquired he of the night before.

" ' Well, darling, you must have been, because I went into your dressing-room and you had stuck strips of sticking-plaster all over the lower part of the looking-glass ! ' " Saying which the inimitable and ever-popular George cried, " *Tableau vivant*—there's a picture for you," and opening his front door, disappeared with all the vitality of a fifth-form schoolboy.

" What a grand man Robey is," said Edward as Alf bid him good night.

" I should think he is. Not only a master of his job but an undefeated sportsman who doesn't know what fear means."

When they arrived at Alf's flat, Edward complained that he had been sleeping badly lately, and asked him if he could lend him something to read which would either help him towards daylight or enable him to woo the twin sister of Death.

Alf ran upstairs and with the optimism of a true artist returned with the manuscript of a new book he had written, and gave it to his friend, confident that Edward would still be enjoying it when the morning tea was brought in. An hour later Edward was reading his friend's effort in bed.

# TWO MEN TALK

The title was certainly provocative, the book being called :

## " THE NAKED TRUTH "

### *Chapter One*

" 2138 ! Only two hundred years ago, and yet owing to the devastating Chemical War of 1942, how little do we lucky people who live in this Utopian age know of Britain and its people, their trials and the primitive times in which they existed.

" Still, from vaults which escaped destruction, from the cellars of ancestral homes, and from the archives of remote places, we are able to gather some slight knowledge of many people who were personalities in the days which have gone and of happenings which belonged to an unenviable past.

" The gathered fragments, however, even when pieced together with the greatest possible care, are naturally by no means accurate, and the history of this period, made up as it is from documents rescued piecemeal from the debris of ruined cities, and corroborated only by word of mouth, have lost much of truth and gained more by exaggeration.

" The Chemical War, which, as we all know, lasted only a week, altered the entire face of the universe. The centuries-old buildings of the world, which were wiped out over-night, no doubt were pleasant if uncomfortable places, and we must take it for granted that the art treasures on which our ancestors prided themselves were of value, though it is difficult to believe that some one of the name of Lutyens could compare with our present day Aloysius Jones, whose vivid colouring in house decoration is a thing at which the nation looks with joy, or that the masterpieces of Germans by the name of Wignor or Wagner and one Slowbert or

Schubert could vie with the two string violin sonatas of our present day Wagstaff Beat. Sculpture, it is said, our forefathers had, but surely nothing to equal the plain granite drinking fountains to be found in every village to-day. Still, as the Britons of 1938 appear to have been for the most part imbeciles, believing as they did in war, the art they possessed was probably too good for them, poor as no doubt these supposed treasures were.

" And, oh ! the discomfort, if what we gather be true, our forbears must have been docile enough to put up with.

" Imagine being without one's own ' Ginjascope.' Fancy having no ' Hypertole ' to hold in one's hand and fly with, and a million other very ordinary things of this kind.

" The wretched people of 1938 had what they called motor cars, smelly conveyances run, I'll trouble you, on a substance called petrol. They were even quite proud of iron engines stuffed with coal which dragged covered wagons called trains on two lines made of iron. It appears, too, they enthused about ridiculous wireless sets, which howled within all that was going on without.

" Then again they ate long dinners, they drank wines, and walked for pleasure. What would they say, I wonder, to our two delicious lozenges which are the soup, fish, meat and sweets all in one. For their amusement, I gather they possessed odd places called theatres, in which hundreds of people were herded together; they knew nothing of our home ' Actordells,' which bring the players to our living-rooms.

" How happy we ought to be to think that we have only to take from our pockets our ' Discapents,' which enable us to see the people we are talking to in the most remote corners of the globe.

# TWO MEN TALK

" There can be no question but that these extraordinary people must have been the most addle-pated species the world has ever known. For instance, their methods of government seems almost beyond belief. They played Politics much as they did a game called Chess. By the way, a set of chessmen has recently been unearthed in the neighbourhood of London, or where London is supposed to have been. It is made up of Qings, Kueens, Frights and Bishops, who were attended by many Prawns.

" To us also it seems incredible that Parliament, instead of being an Imperial Assembly working for the common good, was actually composed of three separate parties, called Conservatives, Liberals and Labour, each with its own battle cry, and all promising the people anything and everything in order that they might be returned to power and be given some hundreds of pounds a year. To-day, as we know, only those with a stake in the country are permitted to record their vote, and then only on some highly controversial matter, but in 1938 everyone, even the mentally deficient, was allowed to go to the polls in the interest of the candidates, who told the most pleasant fairy tales.

" It is small wonder, therefore, that owing to this fantastic state of affairs England at one time nearly became a seventh-rate mildly protesting power, for as you see it was possible for the Prime Minister's two scullery girls to outvote him at the booths.

" Can any of us to-day conceive that in 1938 there were nearly two million unemployed people in England, and that a payment to each, called ' the Dole,' was introduced, being a sum of a hundred millions a year, given to all those who wouldn't or had no work. And then the wages of workers becoming higher and higher, added to the payment

57

of a hundred thousand a day Reparation Debt to America for the World War, and the five key industries of Britain having come to a standstill, the country . . ."

At this point Edward, who took no interest whatever in 2138, "snored off" as the Australians so poetically talk of slumber. The Journalist, as usual, had succeeded where the chemist had failed.

Alf's manuscript fluttered to the floor, never as far as his friend was concerned to find its way even on to a dreamland second-hand barrow with a "Reduced to 2d." mark across its cover. Edward's valet next morning asked him absent-mindedly if he would like a writ with his tea, or some light breakfast port without one.

### ONE NIGHT AT SUPPER

It was only on very rare occasions that the two friends ever came in to their very popular restaurant for supper. They were old enough to dislike the noise and the squash, and both of them felt that it was not necessary for one's pleasure to have food assisted into your mouth by the elbows of strangers, however attractive their owners. Then again, they could not sit remote from all as was their delight at dinner time, for every inch of space being taken after eleven, it was impossible not to hear the conversations of those around them, and in fact difficult not to take a friendly interest in their inane small-talk, or sympathise with the whispering lover, who is always mercifully unaware that his lady is listening to radio messages sent from some one else's eyes.

Still, whenever the two inseparables did break their rule, and became part of the bright respectability and dull immorality which is called the night life of our great city, it cannot be said they were entirely bored. It would have been odd if they had been, for after all, to watch ninety per cent. of one's fellow creatures "pretending" to be everybody except themselves, is extremely funny, and though an expensive amusement, certainly gives the observant onlooker correct labels for nearly all those who are on view.

"I wonder why it is," said Alf, "one meets so very few really natural people to-day. It seems to me that there are not enough galleries for even the most ordinary people to play to. In fact, in public most people seem to act so much for everyone's benefit except the persons they're with, that if you really want to have a good time with your best girl, the thing to do is to let some one else take her out, and then if you arrange to sit at a table within her radius you may be sure she'll give a grand performance *for*, and *to* you, during the entire evening. This, I may tell you, dear Edward, is great fun, for you create a new thrill for yourself by pretending you are stealing your own property, allied to the pleasure every confident lover must feel when he knows he is spoiling his immoralata's evening by making her furious that she is not at his side. Then, again, to bring home to her the fact that she is wasting her night, your eyes should assume an expression of good-natured pity at the efforts of your dreary rival, who incidentally is saving you money by feeding her beautiful face.

"Is it the hour and the lights, the wine and the women, the many, and the music, that make humanity unconscious fun-makers for the 'unseen hosts on High' who look on, and laugh at the antics of the strange little ones who people a world they themselves were once part of," wondered Alf aloud. "Look around you, dear Edward; aren't they a comic lot?"

" They are indeed, old fellow ; and have you ever stopped
to think how very few really amusing men one meets nowadays," mumbled Edward, who had watched laughterless
diners, north, south, east and west of their table. " ' There
was a man, he had a dog,' ' The skies are blue,' and ' There
are milestones on the Dover Road,' may be an illuminating
form of dialogue, but oh ! how I sigh for the shafts that
lit up the darkness when the port made its state entry in
our seldom properly appreciated pre-war days.

" Never was there an evening which did not yield
epigrams on which one could lunch out on the following
morning, but now the funny story or really grand reply,
if it appears, is not doomed for a time to walk the earth—it
is so rare that it lives to become an old friend who when
not on its pet Italian's can, goes through very shame to
the nearest barber to have its face furnishings trimmed."

" My dear Edward," drawled Alf, " this is the first time
I have noticed you showing signs of age. There are just
as many funny fellows about to-day as there used to be,
though their form perhaps is not quite up to what you and
I have been accustomed to. Don't forget that if we dug our
grandfathers up and told them we thought that three-quarters
of the humour of the late 'eighties was to us only laboured
drivel, they would bolt back to their dusty tombs rather
than hobnob, as they felt, with their inane descendants.
But in turning up our noses and yawning at what amused
them, not troubling to understand time and its changes,
we place ourselves entirely and utterly in the wrong."

" Really ! Well, have you ever managed to raise a smile,
drunk or sober, from the considered trifles of the household
wits of long ago ? " asked Edward.

" Perhaps I haven't," replied Alf, " but that is doubtless

no reason that their jokes ought to be given an overdose of twilight sleep. The naughty little jests of the silly 'seventies, which caused every self-respecting pantalette to seek refuge in the seclusion of the crinoline, would not bring the faintest suggestion of a blush to the present-day young lady's over-exposed back, but this is only because the time and place and the girls are different—that's all.

"To say that Lord Chesterfield was 'a wit among Lords, but not a Lord among wits,' is certainly 1938 at its best. Though if you take most of the examples of bygone brilliance out of their period, commencing with the days when Diogenes bored his dog to death and took over his tub as a dwelling, then I grant you that the dialogue in bulk does not seem mirth provoking.

"As a matter of fact, I suppose it is small wonder if the date is not taken into consideration, that open-eyed amaze-ment is shown by present-day Youth when it asks : ' Is that what you laughed at twenty years ago ? ' But, in reality, these young people are as wrong about the past as you are, my dear Edward, when you imagine that we are living to-day in a land quite devoid of humour. Why, only to-night as we came in I heard a fair-haired youth hardly out of his teens discussing a celebrated Armenian author, and bemoaning the fact that much as he was admired, he was careless about appointments and seldom remembered an engagement. ' You can make dates with him,' said the young man, ' but he never keeps them.' ' I don't see why he shouldn't,' replied his companion. ' His ancestors lived on them.' Which is by no means an unworthy reply."

"Yes, I give him full marks for that, Alf.

"I'm glad," said Alf. " By the way, I have just finished reading a book illustrating ' Wit and Humour through the

Ages,' and if you glance at it, dear Edward, you would realise how unwise it is to condemn as simpletons those who laughed at the things of yesterday.

"The stage coach has gone and with it its posting house and ostlers' jest. When the telephone has ceased to be and some other mechanical device called 'the Jing Flink,' perhaps, has taken its place, how do you suppose the little jokes of a present-day operator to another will sound to ears which have only heard of a headphone hidden away in some seldom visited museum. You know the story of the telephone girl ringing up to inquire as to the sex of her sister's baby which had just arrived? You don't. Well, she spoke in the vernacular, and said, 'Is it a transmitter or a receiver?' In years to come, that joke will have to be explained by several profound old gentlemen whose mission in life is to fletcher Sanskrit and undo the wrappings that swathe the widows of Rameses the Second, and then they will be wrong. As you are too well bred, my dear Edward, to laugh at Age and its infirmities, let me entreat you to be as tolerant with the humour of our forbears, as I hope your—I suppose as you are a bachelor I must say, illegitimate—grandchildren will be indulgent to you."

"No doubt you're right," agreed Edward. "You generally are."

"I'm sure I am," said Alf, "and let me impress upon you that Mr. Remembrance should never walk arm-in-arm with Miss Comparison, for unless he is extremely cautious she is a guide who may lead him out of the highways into the dark alleys, which every city holds however beautiful it be. Let Remembrance be happy appreciation of the men we have met and the pleasures we have known, for if we speak of it as such we shall be welcomed as a companion of Youth,

and not as an infernal 'has-been' who begins every other
sentence with 'Ah! in my day.' Nobody wants to know
anything about anybody else's day at any time, and as to
'remembering,' it is impertinent not to realize that nearly
everything connected with most men's lives has happenings
it were far better to forget."

### THE THEATRICAL FIRST NIGHT

"I wonder why they've called the new theatre in Soho
'The Automatic'?" asked Edward.

"I suppose because it will open and shut itself," smiled
Alf, delighted that Edward laughed at the jest, quite
unconscious that it had won a competition in 1860, coupled
with an epitaph on a boarding-house keeper's tombstone—
"Let Bygones be Rissoles."

"Are you going to the first night there to-morrow?"
inquired Edward.

"I don't think so, dear boy; I hate first nights. I long
ago dubbed the audience who attend them 'The Death Watch.'
Most of them go hoping for the worst and fearing for the
best. Added to which, if you assist, as they say, on these
occasions, you are always accused of having got a laugh
during one of the intervals by saying something brilliantly
unkind, which you haven't, although of course you wish
you had. No, I make a point of going on the second night,
if there is one, though of course to expect such a thing
nowadays is to be slightly optimistic."

"Oh, I rather like the excitement of a first night." ventured
Edward. "It's true you always see exactly the same people,
but that in itself amuses me. For one becomes quite an old
friend of the women's dresses, and it's good fun to watch

the aigrette of the spring getting more soiled and scantier towards December. The dinner jackets of the critics, too, are not without interest, shining as they do as brightly as the articles their wearers hope to write. In fact, the personnel of the stalls is an entertainment in itself, made up as it is of authors whom one wishes one had left unread, pansies whom one would willingly pay to have bedded out in some other country, to say nothing of Society looking like the back row of the chorus, and the chorus looking exactly like the front row of Society. The hard-working rich and the idle poor sit cheek by jowl on these occasions, the poor having paid and the rich having cadged, all of them sure, of course, that on *their* judgment, and theirs alone, the fate of the evening depends.

"The Death Watch is divided into many groups. First of all there are 'the enthusiasts,' and while they are in the minority, they are ready to applaud, even before the curtain rises, indeed, they would be almost sure to put their hands together if it never went up at all. In this more often than not they would be wise. Then there are 'the fans,' who imagine they are at a football match, shouting encouragement to their favourites if they gain a laugh or a tear, much as the men from Manchester scream when Cottonopolis has obtained a free kick at the Arsenal or a goal from Chelsea United. On the other hand, many of these first-nighters arrive quite unprejudiced and to show their impartiality hiss and clap at the same time."

"The people I think so tiresome at the theatre," said Alf, "are the flappers who fill their mouths with chocolates, hold their boy friend's right hand with their left, and so make it impossible for either of them to laugh or applaud."

"I don't see why they can't applaud," said Edward.

# TWO MEN TALK

" Don't you ? " said Alf. " The other night I saw a couple trying to get enthusiastic without letting go of each other, if I may put it so, and the result was that the young man's left missed his girl friend's right, and she received such a slap on the bosom that she left her seat feeling extremely faint."

" Do you think the Cinemas are killing the Theatre, Alf ? Many people do ! "

" They don't know what they're talking about, old boy," said the Journalist, whose work was to a very large extent bound up with the play-house. " How can anything mechanical ever take the place of flesh and blood. Besides, people don't go to the films nowadays as they used to, just because they *are* films, they only go if they are good films ; if they are bad they stay away. What has done harm to the Theatre is not the films or any other sort of rival enter-tainment. It is the dearth of good plays, the continual sex rubbish, bad language, questionable jokes that one hears handed out, and the sight of women with hardly a stitch on. The real people of this country don't want muck, my dear fellow, and the real people are the vast majority of playgoers. The minority who delight in dirt are not enough to keep any theatre open successfully for three weeks."

" I never can understand," said Edward, " why some comedians use language on the stage and rely on jokes that in nine cases out of ten haven't even a clever double meaning. The supposed humour of some of the so-called comic men in cabaret to-day is a matter for the police. Do you know, Alf, I am thinking seriously of starting an ' Anti-Dirt Club.' All members visiting a Cabaret and hearing filth talked will have to pledge themselves to throw anything from custard pies to empty bottles at the ruffians who would be better

65

in a sewer, and also to slap the faces of the foreign pimps who pay them. But, reverting to Films, my dear Edward, and for the time being forgetting the Theatre, the work of the great film producers is a thing at which one may well sit lost in amazement. They need and possess not only the constructive qualities of the premier dramatists, but a knowledge of composition such as is found only in the galleries where rests for ever the work of those whose paintings will live when dynasties are forgotten.

"Of course to-day there are many great directors, but in the early days of the Talkies there were some wild and wonderful gentlemen, who in the chaos which ensued when the silent film ceased to be, found themselves directing pictures. Many of them were quite incompetent and would not have been allowed to produce even a one-act play on the stage; besides which, most of them were hopelessly common, and although they knew exactly what they wanted, they couldn't spell it. Some of the others, if there had been four H's in Hollyhocks, would have dropped them with the ease a bankrupt is dropped by his best friends. The story is told of one of this fraternity who, having bought the rights of a banned novel, was told that it would be impossible for him to make a film treatment of it, because the story was one which dealt with Lesbians. All he said blandly was, 'Well, what does that matter; let us make them Austrians.'

"The limited knowledge of the French language possessed by these noblemen was oddly enough often a slight drawback when they were dealing with scenes laid at the once fashionable Monte Carlo, now given over to Blackpool on holiday.

"The following are the directions given to an actor as to what he had to do by one of these supposed thoroughly knowledgable disciples of Reinhardt; he said, 'Now, ole boy, yer see you're at Monte Carlo, see, and yer one of the Crooperers at the gaming tables, see. Yer stands up in front of this 'ere wheel and yer spins it, see, and then when it gets going yer chucks this 'ere ball on to the basin as it whirls round and then you shouts in French to the gamblers, " Mesdames and Moosieurs, *Plat du Jour*." ' "

" Good for you, Alf, old man," said the usual listener. " If I were asked what I should do with linguists of that sort I'd reply as did the stranger who was asked by an lady pianist what he thought of her execution; he said, ' I am all for it ! ' "

" But to return to the question of the Theatre and the Cinema, it is not to be denied that while a good play will always hold its own, the entertainment provided by the screen has given the theatre a mortal blow, not as its rival in the art of the Theatre as such, but as something which provides for the great mass of the people a thing at which they may well marvel and from which they can derive infinite pleasure."

" You know a great many people connected with film-land, don't you, Alf ? " asked Edward.

" Yes, my dear fellow. I've tumbled up against most of them in the course of my job, and on the whole I have found the majority of them charming people, whose only weakness is to live looking at life through camera angles."

" And their conceit insufferable, I suppose," chimed in Edward.

" There you are entirely wrong. They may be made look ridiculous by paid boosters, who are as a rule dangerous lunatics believing that publicity of any kind is good simply because it *is* publicity—but they themselves are quite all right.

" Don't forget that the greatest names handed down

to us through the ages would only be remembered as figures of fun if we were informed by salaried yes-men that they drank iced hock at four every morning out of specially grown melons, that they swam in silver-lined bathing pools a mile long, for which Cartier supplied real gold-fish with emerald eyes, or that their lunches consisted of quails brought for them in aeroplanes twice a week from the Soudan to the Pacific slope.

"What do you suppose we should think of Napoleon if we were told and believed that he sang to a harp and ate rose leaves on the field of Austerlitz, on returning to his tent to write his despatches in his sleep. And yet this is the parallel balderdash to be read daily of some of the most simple and ordinary people who happen to have become world celebrities on the screen.

"Take, for instance, Douglas Fairbanks, Leslie Howard, Ronald Colman, Clive Brook, William Powell, and a host of other favourites, who couldn't think of behaving like anything but very direct human beings. Yet heaven knows what the paragraphists would try to make us swallow about them ; among other things probably that Mr. Colman has not only refused the proffered hands in marriage of all the half-crown royalties in Europe, but that he has a fan mail of twenty thousand letters a day, which he answers personally in long-hand, while as for Mr. Fairbanks, they would think nothing of trying to make us believe that he flies after lunch to shoot a lion or two in Africa, when probably all he has done is to have taken a walk up to the Zoo or had a cup of tea at Lyons' Corner House.

"George Arliss, whom I know well, great artist that he is, is gentle and modest to a degree. Oh, and my dear fellow, a dozen others.

# TWO MEN TALK

" I can't say I know many whose names are household words, but those I have met have been anything but what you would suppose them to be by reading the nonsense about them doled out daily to an eager-for-sensation public."

Alf began to wax enthusiastic in his defence of the screen artists he knew, and who for business reasons were unable to shout out, " Don't believe a word of what you read about me. I never eat ortolons' tongues on toast for breakfast. I love bloaters. I haven't got a private Pullman Car—I always travel third-class. My underclothes are not studded with rubies and diamonds. I buy them at Harrods," and as one star after another was discussed, the name of his greatest favourite, Norma Shearer, fell lovingly from his lips.

" Now, my dear Edward, there is to me one of the most charming and delightful women it has ever been my lot to meet."

" I like her pictures awfully," said Edward.

" Like them ? " roared Alf. " Like ? Say you are crazy about her work and then I shall insist for once on paying for our dinner. She's divine ! "

" Better than Garbo, better than Chatterton, better than Dietrich. Is that what you are going to say ? " said Edward.

" I am not comparing anyone with anyone, Edward. I'm saying she's divine. I don't pretend I'm not prejudiced— I am, because I've met her. Give me another drink. Gentle-mannered, marvellous poise, a most sweet and gracious lady if ever there was one. She's a Canadian, has two children, was married to one of the most brilliant men in the American film industry, alas ! to the regret of his thousands of friends, no more—and—and——"

Edward stared so hard at Alf that Alf stopped.

" What's the matter ? " he inquired.

" Nothing. I was only wondering if you weren't qualify-ing for the press agent you were talking of just now."

" Oh, shut up ! " said Alf. " You're going all British. What's the good of living if you can't be enthusiastic and show it. Hate well, love well, work well and slack well. That's my motto. I'm Norma Shearer's greatest British fan, and why shouldn't I say so. It mayn't do her any good, but it pleases me—so that's that."

" But surely," said Edward, " performing on the screen is *behaving*, not acting."

" In the case of the celluloid blonde, this is true," said Alf, " but every hour brings screen production nearer per-fection, and though you may look with good-natured toler-ance at an obviously well-directed puppet, where, taking only one instance, could you find a more consistent and masterly performance on any stage than the acting of Paul Muni in the character of Pasteur ? It may not possess the compelling magic of the mighty Lucien Guitry in the same part, but it is in itself an inimitable stage performance which runs the gamut of the emotions over the entire period of the scientist's life, in so faultless a manner that this actor takes you by the hand and makes you part of Pasteur's family circle. That the screen will ever be a medium for the tragic intensity and vitality of a Kean or a Garrick in highly debatable, but that it is capable, in the hands of a great artist, of compelling tears as well as laughter, shows how far a new art has travelled, and who knows how far it may travel apart from the work of the stars themselves ? "

At this moment a majestic blonde, looking like a Christmas tree in summertime, sailed out into the open past their table.

" That's chemical Flora," whispered Alf.

" Oh, is that what's she called ? "

" Yes, amongst other things," answered the knowing one. " She's the little sweetheart who after her fourth marriage invented that famous game, called ' Coming Events.' "

" I don't follow you," said Edward. " Is it something that cast a shadow before her ? "

" Don't be silly, Edward. She plays *ingénues*. No, it's a delightfully easy pastime and makes definitely for good because it avoids confusion when the organ is being strummed for nuptial musical chairs. You see, Flora has been married seven times and for her last three virginal excursions she invented as I tell you ' Coming Events,' rule one being the sending out of invitations for her next divorce with the wedding cake. This thoughtfulness on her part not only saved her postage but incidentally informed the Happy Bridegroom, as he trod the aisle she knew so well, exactly where he ' got off.'

" It is only natural, of course, dear Edward, that the poor gentleman imagined as he clasped Flora in his arms that he had secured a freehold, but in reality he awakened to find that she only granted short leases, the length of which depended largely on the matured advice of her publicity agent.

" You mustn't forget that all the large family of Floras marry in haste and divorce with pleasure," continued Alf.

" Why they ever trouble to get married at all is what beats me, and how for the umpteenth time they dare face even the best judges that money can buy is a thing to marvel at," bleated Edward.

" Oh, well, dear boy, I've no doubt they take good cover behind the blushes they hide in the top drawer of their dressing-tables, which they keep there to help them give new reasons for rifts in their domestic life."

" What are the usual grounds these nit-wits give for divorce, Alf? "

" Oh, as long as they *are* grounds, even the ones to be found in the morning coffee are enough, I believe, to satisfy the professional home-breakers at Reno."

Alf remembered that the particular Flora who had just melted into space was originally married to a cameraman.

The marriage became " obscura " because she did not approve of his double exposures.

" Mental cruelty, of course, is very fashionable. It seems an extremely optimistic plea to me, as the Floras of the world are very nearly brainless.

" Amongst the best selected which the platinum blonde who has just passed us, dear Edward, chose as a temporary mate, was a French Marquis—not the sort of *marquee* which you go into when it come on to rain, but a real live nobleman of ancient lineage, one of those perfect gentlemen who are willing to make anyone a lady so long as they have a large enough banking account.

" The motto beneath his crest was ' *Sans peur et sans reproche.*' When he went broke and Flora flung him into the gutter from which he had picked her up, he journeyed for a long time on the even ' tenner ' of other people's money.

" At one period of his disasters he was starving, and earned the approbation of those of his brother aristocrats, who also lived by disposing of unconsidered titles, for with great good humour he altered the wording beneath the crest of his ancestors to, ' *Sans beurre et sans brioche.* ' "

" I wonder," said Edward, looking across the room at a once beautiful actress, " if there is anything so finished as a finished artist."

" Nothing," said Alf. " And I always think it is so sad

to see the lines on their faces which ought to be in their parts, all because when they were acting they would insist on counting their houses before they were hatched."

" She looks extremely weary," said Edward. " Why, I wonder ? The pale-faced youth who is with her is very rich."

" Isn't that the reason, old fellow ? But what's far worse is that the gent you're looking at is a direct descendant of the Tudors and writes plays ! "

" My God, don't say that."

" He does, other people's."

" This, I suppose, is the result of his having won a prize at Eton for reciting ' I remember.' I'm sorry he's dull though," sighed Edward. " I had thought of asking them both to lunch to-morrow."

" I shouldn't," replied Alf, " because apart from anything else, he has consumption and she has a *matinée*."

### A WEEK LATER

An American, on being asked, " How do you like our English summer ? " replied, " I don't know—I was in bed both days."

It must have been one of these two days (for it was extremely hot) that Alf and his shadow were lolling over dinner. The evening had not started too well, for Edward early on had been mistaken for a waiter by a gentleman who, resplendent in new dress clothes, to which he had added three studs, a bunch of seals, a red handkerchief and a buttonhole, made up of a moss rose and maidenhair fern, had said to him brusquely, " Hi ! where can I wash ? " to which Edward had replied somewhat tersely, "All over if you like."

While Alf had been equally annoyed by a witty bloke who, as he put it, had scored off him heavily. It happened that Alf, in his most hearty manner, had greeted him, saying, "My dear fellow, how are you? I haven't seen you for over a year." To which the gent, who turned out to be a perfect stranger, replied, "How good of you!" and this after Alf had threaded his way through so many Belisha Beacons that he felt like nothing so much as a riderless competitor in a gymkhana at Allahabad, or some other equally bad Indian station.

They were lolling, as we know, when Edward delivered himself of that by no means original but brainy remark, "I wonder where all the amusing stories come from?" The answer, of course, is engraved on stone. It is, "Oh, from the Stock Exchange!" but Alfred, throwing convention to the winds, gurgled, "That question, my dear fellow, was asked by Nero of Balbus, who paused in his Winston-like leisure of building a wall to tell the latest chestnut to the most remembered violinist of all time. It is a question which ranks in antiquity with such classic small talk as ' Hock is such a clean wine,' or ' All dogs are fond of me,' and a few other inane remarks without which the social idiot would be dumb, and children's copy books without anything for them to copy.

" Why, dear Edward, may I inquire, do you suddenly become so inquisitive?—why puzzle our brains as to who made up the amusing stories that, born in the days of Chaucer, have been told in togas and in tights and have weathered the brocade of a Surface, the knee-breeches of a Brummell, and limped home to us to-day, via Anne, Victoria and the late King Edward of blessed and affectionate memory? "

74

# TWO MEN TALK

"For no particular reason, my old china, as the Tommies used to say in the war," said Edward, looking his florid friend straight in the eye and wondering how many years alcohol was ahead of him and he ahead of a fit, "other than that I happened to have heard one or two rather amusing things lately and I thought they might make you laugh, that's all."

"Fire away, then," said Alf.

"You'll stop me if you know them, won't you?"

"Don't be silly. You're perfectly certain I should never be so ill-bred as to do that, so why waste your breath by delivering yourself of another classic. It's only the honest Johns from Yorkshire who, priding themselves on hurting people for their own good, ask them to lunch at the Palace of Truth. Well, you know my name's not John, that I was not born in Yorkshire, and that as regards honesty I am no more honest than the company I keep, so why, I ask you, do you invite me to spoil the pleasure you insist on giving yourself at my expense by saying 'Stop me,' as if I were a gentleman with a tricycle laden with ices. Even if I am the author of your oldest anecdote I shall not complain, for it is quite possible that it has been to the tailor's and is so decked out in a new suit that it will be by no means an unwelcome visitor. Tell me them all, for you, dear Eddy, are my friend, and a friend can do no wrong, even if he remembers to pay back the money he has borrowed."

"Old heart," said Edward, "my little tales are perfectly excellent and as good wine needs no push, so my stories require no apologies. If you don't like them you go and buy that famous little book, 'How to be funny on a pound a week.' You'll probably be able to dine out on it for a considerable time, though naturally not nearer London than Hampstead."

75

"You're weakening, Edward," laughed Alf.   "You're afraid I shall know all your tit-bits and you're getting cold feet."

"Not at all, old boy."

"Well, go on," yawned Alf.

"Why not," said Edward.   "Did you ever hear of the young lady who went into a chemist's shop in Aberdeen?"

"No," replied our accommodating Alf.

"Well, on leaving the establishment—she forgot to pick up her change—the shop assistant, who was honesty itself, tried as she walked down the street to attract her attention by tapping on the window with a powder puff."

"Noisy girl," said Alf, "but I wonder why it is that Aberdeen, one of the most beautiful cities in the Empire—from a granite point of view—should have all the stories connected with economic thought pinned to its grey breast?"

"I suppose, dear fellow, they were invented by the only Jew who tried to earn a living there.   He left starving, you know."

"Oh, did he?   And, of course, walking?"

"I suppose so.   I always think that hiking, even for pleasure, is the dullest of all amusements," said Edward. "But padding the hoof makes me think of trains . . ."

"Oh!" again yawned Alf.

"Yes, did you ever hear the story of the three men who went to Victoria Station to catch one, and having to wait there some time negotiated more than several drinks in the refreshment room?"

"No," said Alf.

"Well, all of them being somewhat unsteady as the express was about to leave, a porter bundled the two nearest him into a first-class compartment just as the whistle blew. When the train was well out of sight the man who was left behind suddenly said to the young man who had been so extremely kind to his companions, 'My hat, what have you done? Do you know what you've done?' 'No, sir,' answered the porter, "what *have* I done?' 'You've put my friends into the train.' 'Well, why not?" said the porter. 'Why not!' shouted the inebriated gentleman, 'why not? Those two fellows came to see me off!'"

"That's quite good, dear boy, so you deserve one in return," laughed Alf. "It's about a gentleman who went into the smartest of smart Fruit Shops in this wonderful city of ours. I don't know if you know it, and I really don't mind if you do, dear Edward, because I am determined to tell it you."

"If you say so," smiled Edward.

"Well, this brave man walked in where millionaires fear to tread and asked for a pear. Wrapped in the most beautiful tissue paper, one was presented to him by a charming damsel, who held out her hand and said, 'Seven-and-six, if you please, sir.' 'Good heavens, seven-and-sixpence! What a price,' thought our hero as he gave the ox-eyed peroxide beauty a ten shilling note. Smilingly she offered him his half-crown change. 'Oh, no!' said the possessor of the pear, 'please keep it. I trod on a grape as I came in.'"

"Excellent," said Edward, and immediately asked Alf if the story of the little Cockney boy and the pencils was a chestnut.

"No, old man."

"Well, it's by no means bad. At school one morning the mistress asked him if he had any pencils.

"'No,' replied the boy, 'I ain't got no pencils.' To which the lady said, 'You mustn't say "I ain't got no pencils" —that's not good grammar—you must say:

"'No, *I* have no pencils,

*He* has no pencils,

*She* has no pencils,

*We* have no pencils,
*You* have no pencils,
*They* have no pencils.'

" ' Oh, really,' said the boy.    ' Well then, where the hell
*are* all the pencils ? ' "

After a moment's pause, Edward rather diffidently observed
that although he had never said much that was worth record-
ing, he did take some little credit for remarks made to two
different gentlemen, both of whom were his fellow travellers
on a voyage to that country of countries, South Africa.

" And what may these epoch-making observations be ? "
inquired Alf.

" I did not say they were epoch-making," said Edward.
" I only meant they were fairly good.   One evening I
entered the smoking-room of the great liner on which I was
travelling, and the weather being somewhat chilly, as we had
not yet reached Madeira, I inquired of a stout little man
seated near the door if he objected to my having the windows
closed on our side of the bar.   Instead of meeting, as I
expected, with a cheery ' Of course not,' I was met with a
veritable tirade from the gentleman.   ' Shoot t'window ? '
he bawled in a grand north-country accent, ' nay, I won't
'ave it shoot.   I've come out on this 'ere hocean foer
fresh hair, and I do hobject very strongly.   You shan't
shoot 'oop window—if yer don't want hair, go elsewhere.
I 'appen to want hair and I am going to 'ave it.'   There was
nothing to be said, so all I could do was to find other accommo-
dation.   Before doing so, however, I asked the steward who
this very objectionable gentleman might be.

" ' Oh,' said the dispenser of pink gin and other poisons,
' that is Mr. Wills.   He owns a fleet of trawlers and is known
in the north as the " Herring King." ' "

" ' Oh, is he ? ' I replied. Without much more ado, I walked up to the little man and said, ' I understand you are the Herring King ? ' to which he shouted, ' I ham, and what about it ? ' ' I really don't know,' I replied. ' The only thing that's worrying me is whether I shall have a *hard* row or a *soft* row with you.'

" May I say, dear Alf, that I gave myself several marks for the thought."

" You're quite right. And what may be the other brilliant epigrammatic exercise you place to your credit, dear fellow ? "

" Well, it was one which I think might pass muster. A lank-looking individual on the same ship approached me the first morning out at sea, and without waiting for an introduction of any kind, slapped me on the back and informed me that his name was Smith and he was a traveller—a commercial traveller, he continued, travelling in *castor oil*. To which I said I could think of no better opening for a conversation."

" That was quite good," said Alf. " I think you'd better make the sea your home ; I have yet to hear you even slightly funny on shore."

" I wonder if during the War you remember reading of a bomb that only missed Charing Cross Hospital by a few yards ? "

" No, I don't think I do," said Edward.

" Well, it made a tremendous hole in the roadway, and as I stood looking at it two quite funny things happened. I noticed an obvious German contemplating the damage for some time and then, shaking his head, he murmured sadly, ' Dis is not de way to vin de voer.' He had hardly strolled off despondently towards the Strand, disgusted with the inaccurate bomb-dropping of his countrymen, when I saw a woman walking towards me with a baby in her arms, which was screaming its lungs out. To try and quieten the little angel its mother danced it gently up and down, saying, 'now then, there, there, there, don't cry, be a good child. Come along —stop crying—come along, stop crying like a darling, and I'll show you what the naughty bomb has done."

" I'm beginning to think, Alf, old man, that your stories are a bit better than mine," said Edward.

" Fifty-fifty, perhaps, up to now," said the Pastel magnanimously, " how do you like this one : ' Oh ! ' said the lady of the house, entering the kitchen. ' Look, cook, look ! Spring has arrived. Summer will soon be here now.' ' Why do you say that, mum ? ' asked the cook. ' Because the tortoise has come out of his long sleep and crawled from under the dresser. Look at him ! ' ' What ! ' said the cook, ' is that a tortoise ? ' ' Yes,' said the payer of wages, ' why do you ask ? ' ' Well, mum, I never knew it was a tortoise. I've been cracking the coals with it all the winter.' "

" I think we'd better stop now, don't you, or we shall have none left for another day, as children say when they've booked too many return tickets for the jam cupboard."

" If you say so, old man, but as we are drinking there is quite a good little tale about vintage port which might hand you a laugh."

" What is it ? "

" It's about a very rich old sportsman who invited his impecunious nephew to dine with him. The youth was extremely nervous, as he was quite conscious that his uncle, whom he hardly knew, was weighing him up. All through the meal, however, he weathered the storm and managed to answer fairly correctly the many questions his elderly relation put to him. As a connoisseur of wine, however, he didn't shine quite so brightly. ' Do you like port, my boy ? ' said the uncle. ' I do,' said the nephew. ' Well, what do you think of the bottle we're attacking, eh?' 'Oh, excellent, uncle.' 'Plenty of body to it, eh?' 'Oh yes, uncle.' 'Now, my boy, you seem very knowledgable, *what is it*, do you think?' The young man tasted it, again thought for a moment, and then said, ' 48.' 'No, my boy, it's 49.' 'Oh! is it, uncle, ; well, that's not so bad, I was only a shilling wrong, wasn't I?' "

At this moment the band, which had been extraordinarily loud all the evening, became suddenly piano, which encouraged Alf to ask one of the head waiters to thank the conductor for being so thoughtful and to say how difficult it was for those who hated noise to be epigrammatic during even the most artistic drum solo. " Oh, certainly, sir, I will tell the band what you say, sir," said the man whose stock phrase for impatient customers was always " They are cooking it special for you, sir."

A man whom both Alf and Edward knew extremely well passed them by with a nod without even pausing to say " Good evening ! "

" It's extraordinary, Alf, isn't it, why some fellows are so uncertain. They know you one day and not the next."

" I always like them best on the next," said Alf, " don't you? "

" Perhaps, but how do you account for the behaviour of these people? Shyness, do you think? "

" No, that's the alibi in ninety-nine cases out of a hundred for infernal conceit or real bad manners. Shyness is by no means a common complaint and is confined generally to those who as young men have been content to drink water, eat apples and admire postcards sold surreptitiously at the corner of the Rue de Rivoli."

" You can't get away from the fact, though, Alf, that Englishmen are fairly stand-offish with strangers, aren't they? "

" Well, but of course they are, and so they should be. I don't believe in all this ' How are you ? Welcome to our city ! ! ! ' stuff from men who greet you as a long-lost brother simply because you both happen to be breathing the same square yard of air."

" Yes, I agree. But as a nation I *do* think we go a bit over the odds in not confining our domes of silence to our kitchen chairs."

" Edward, my boy, I long ago discovered that the world is made up of sixty per cent. of natural people, ten per cent. of shy ones, ten per cent. of snobs, and twenty per cent. of idiots."

" Be thankful for those who are natural ;
Be tolerant of the shy ;
Give the snobs a good swift kick in the pants.
And bless the idiots, for they will never find you out."

" But, talking of people putting on side, edge, or whatever name these monkey antics go by, will you explain to my why anybody living can be such an ass as to be conceited about anything ? I'll eat my hat," said Alf, " if you can.

" Life at its best is only a somewhat erratically run railway system which issues single tickets for a terminus to which few of us want to go. Our lot on earth is to sit in the same waiting-room wondering on which train we are booked. This being so, is there anything very clever if you or I have been able to edge nearer to the fireplace than the other fellow ? Not a bit of it.

" Those who are more fortunate than their fellows are pushed or stumble towards the grate. Believe me, it is not by any particular cleverness of his own that Jones is more comfortably situated than Smith, and even if it were so it would be well if Jones remembered that this planet we call the World is little more than a grain of sand on a Sahara of a Sahara of Sands. So if he will add that up, and having done so can still take any pride in his infinitesimal achievements on the decimal part of a decimal something in space, then the poor gentleman should be put into a cage and fed with apples on the end of a stick."

" Quite right," said Edward.

" And if by any chance," continued Alf, " you fall in with some one who is so conceited that he is insufferable you would be quite entitled to bring him up with a round turn by saying, ' Sir, you seem to have forgotten that all men smell alike in their coffins ! ' "

There was a pause for thought after this remark, and then Alf said suddenly, " Have you read ' The Citadel,' Edward, because if not do, it is brilliant."

" It's an attack on doctors in general, isn't it ? "

" Certainly not—it is a story in which a very small proportion of the Medical Profession are accused of being humbugs, and this fact, when proved, is the salvation of the leading personage who lives between the covers of this masterpiece of progressive construction. But because some of the characters *are* individual humbugs—and are shown as such—this book does not set out to be an attack on a wide front. It crucifies the humbug, that's all. And you're not going to tell me that there are *not* medical humbugs, are you ? There are humbugs in every walk of life. Indeed, sometimes, when the days are dark, it is difficult to realize that the world itself isn't all humbug."

" A doctor to me is as sacred as a priest," said Edward ; " we place him on a pedestal and there he should remain ; I hope you agree, Alf."

"I do, indeed, that's why I abominate seeing medical students dressed up in fantastic costumes, collecting money in the streets."

" Means to an end, Alf."

" Nonsense, old son, these young men are some day to
be sentinels standing guard at our bedsides—when, as John
Bright put it, ' The wings of the Angel of Death are ' etc.,
etc., therefore of all people they are the last who should
make Tomfools of themselves in public.  I don't want to see
the Bland Suttons and the Horders of to-morrow rushing about
the Metropolis, dressed up as Red Indians and Cowboys.  From
the moment they pass the threshold of their hospital as students
they should be as far apart from their fellows as the lay
brother in a monastery, who is qualifying for greater things."

" Yes, I'd never thought of that," said Edward.   " But,
speaking of this book you tell me to read, I suppose there is a
certain amount of forgivable humbug among medical men ? "

" Well, of course—for to be a really successful doctor
you must be an extraordinarily good actor.  Though I'm
bound to say I don't care much for the exaggerated bedside
manner adopted by many of them.   When they overdo it
it is impossible to gather whether you ought to be up and
about, or inviting the undertaker to lunch."

" Yes ; and what I dislike intensely is that remnant of the
early Wimpole Street renaissance—the keeping of the patient
waiting ; it makes me by no means pleased," joined in Edward.

" And, heavens, how I hate some of the servants who open
the front doors of the houses in which medical men practice.
Most of them maidens of uncertain years, look at you with
a ' come into the morgue' expression on their faces," said Alf.
" They frighten me to death, and make me tremble in the waiting-room as I sit reading last year's *Punch* upside down.  Every
doctor's servant ought to be, if not a comedian, at least some
one with comedy instincts, while the master, if he can't smile
cheerily, ought to go to Selfridge's and buy himself one."

# TWO MEN TALK

## THE YEAR CREPT ON

It was August—again August not so many years since 1914 and yet —— !

" Have you seen the evening paper ? " said Edward.

" Yes," replied the scribbler, " I read it at breakfast."

" Well, do you realise that people are talking quite glibly about the possibility of our going to war ? "

" I do, old man. I notice that those extraordinary patriots who are so anxious that you and I should die for their country are at it again. But really, I shouldn't stare in utter amazement, Edward. Remember that a man who can be surprised at anything after he has reached the age of fifty should be led around the country and shown on fair-grounds as a rival to the bearded lady or the skeleton dude as something to marvel at."

" Perhaps," said Edward, " it might be arranged that these fighting politicians who dislike travelling in war-time should be sent out to the front to open the batting."

" Not a bad idea, old boy, because if this were the case it is very possible that hostilities might be delayed indefinitely."

" That's a certainty," said Edward.

" But," Alf continued thoughtfully, " do you realize that there is going *to be no ' Front' in the next war*—at any rate, not ' the Front ' as we knew it in '14.

" *The ' Front' will be in every capital city in the world.* You can take it from me that the people in London, Paris or Berlin will not be waiting for news from their armies in the Field—the armies in the Field will be waiting to hear how many of their wives and children and sisters and brothers have been bombed to death each evening in the peaceful homes they have left behind.

"Oh yes, old fellow, that's one thing about the next war—the lunatics who decide to have it will be well gassed with the rest of us, and not the sort of gas, mind you, that they themselves specialize in at their various Parliament Houses."

"Well," said Edward, "it's a jolly good thing in looking back on it all that we won it."

"Won what?"

"Won the Great War."

"What did you say we'd done?"

"Won it," said Edward.

"I see," said Alf, with a look which seemed to say, "I had no idea I was dining with a congenital idiot."

Memory is a river on which it is never wise to sail one's boat. The banks which hold it fast are strewn with withered flowers of regret, while quite impossible of capture float past the little craft we call our life, the saddest of all things—the many might-have-beens which once were ours."

"I quite agree," said Edward. "Let us forget 1914, anyway for this evening."

"Right. Mind you," said Alf, brightening up, "I don't mind thinking of the many amusing things which happened in those awful times. For instance, the spy scare complex was responsible for much that went to assist the gaiety of the nation.

"Why, I remember a most respectable grocer in the suburbs being given a hiding while he was exercising his two dogs, because they happened to be Dachshunds."

"Well, we were all on edge, weren't we, Alf, and as the most innocent looking bush was supposed to harbour a battalion of German agents—everyone became extremely cautious. Do you remember the answer an old cockney lady on the top of an Embankment bus gave to a male stranger when she was asked by him if that was the River Thames. She looked at him with the icy stare of a hire purchase refrigerator and simply replied, 'Don't ask me, I don't know.'

"Of all the minor miseries we went through during the war I think the thing that got on my nerves more than anything else," remarked Edward, "was all the crawling about in the dark we had to put up with for four years. I am bound to say I didn't mind being bombed so much—the chances were any odds against you being hit—but to be unable to see a single thing when night came and having to grope one's way up once familiar streets almost by compass, was perfectly foul. I remember I swore that when peace was declared I'd sit in a room lit by million candle-power lights, eat white bread and butter and drink lashings of champagne, and I did!"

"Yes, you're quite right, the bombing was exciting and made me more angry than frightened," Alf thought aloud. "But, talking of being frightened, there wasn't a money-lender left in London, was there? The Palestine Express took them all to Brighton, where I can only suppose they were reduced to lending good Christian money to each other."

"Why didn't they conscript these Hitler Hussars, Alf?"

"Old man, the War Office came to the conclusion that they would be no good as soldiers, for they felt that if they were told to charge they'd overcharge, and not one of them would advance without security.

"Sacha Guitry has some wonderful stories about the war," said Edward, "but it's no good repeating them in English, they lose their point—and my French is atrocious."

"What a grand man is Sacha—a cynic with a child-like smile and a wit that tears his foes to tatters.

" His father, the great Lucien, could also be devastating on occasion," said Alf, calling to mind an interview he had had with that mighty artist in 1916. " An American actor had been given the Legion of Honour for appearing in Paris at a charity Red Cross *matineé* as *Macbeth*. This struck me as very odd," continued Alf, " and I ventured to ask M. Lucien why this very ordinary performer had been so greatly honoured. ' Ah ! ' said the monarch of all he surveyed in theatreland, ' I will tell you,' and his eyes twinkled mischievously as he whispered, ' They gave it to him because he only did it *once* ! ' "

" Talking of our soldiers, Alf," said Edward, " harking back to the grim side of things, a volume as large as the *Encyclopædia Britannica* could easily be filled if all the stories were written of our brave fellows at the front.

" I wonder what other men who ever lived would have had the nerve and humour to find affectionately comic names for the engines designed for their own destruction as did our Tommies ? Why, with shrapnel bursting over them, they laughed, and shouted out, ' Have another go, Jerry, you ain't quite got the range,' and it was a British soldier who, after ten days in the trenches, was found sitting with a newspaper cutting pegged up in front of him on which was printed ' Business as Usual.' "

The two friends didn't laugh at the memory. Admiration and merriment seldom go hand in hand.

" Then there was that typical story of a grand Bond Street lad, a youth in the Irish Guards, who was unable to locate a body of German Infantry whose rifle fire was playing havoc with our fellows. Do you remember it, Edward ? "

" No, I don't think so, Alf."

" Well, his men wanted to charge anywhere, right, left

or centre to find the Jerrys and '*put it across them*,' as they said, at close quarters. Knowing this would mean that they would probably be wiped out, our hero commanded them all to lie down and said, 'I will find them alone. When you see them, fire!' Much against their will his men fell on their faces. The officer shouted 'Waiter!' Like a flash two hundred Huns jumped up from their cover, and not one of them ever served bacon and eggs in England again.

"Poor devils, I don't suppose they wanted the war any more than our fellows did. And when you come to think of our lads it's marvellous," reflected Alf, "how the rank and file stuck it and grumbled so little.

"Even when the food tasted peculiar on one occasion, the only remark that was heard from a cockney boy whose palate was a trifle more delicate than that of his pals, was, 'I say, my old China, you might tell Lord Kitchener, with my compliments, that if this 'ere Irish stew has to be made with petrol, then I prefers the best petrol.'

"I wonder, Edward, if you remember the story of the Tommy in hospital and the Duchess, turned nurse, who spent several hours each day holding the hands of the convalescents."

"I don't know that I do," replied Edward, "what was it?"

"The well-meaning lady of title, who was as competent to nurse as I am to make a violin, used to go her daily round of the wards, sitting on the end of the beds and in a most praiseworthy way doing all she could to cheer up the boys, by writing letters for them and keeping up a running fire of chatty inanity in an endeavour to take their minds off their wounds. On her arrival at a newcomer's couch she always commenced her conversation by saying, 'And where were you hit, dear man?' to which she usually received the answer she expected, which was that the poor fellow had been knocked over on the Somme, or at Arras or Ypres or wherever the Hun had straffed him, but she was somewhat embarrassed one morning when on saying to a soldier, whom she had never seen before, ' And where were you hit, dear man,' she was answered by our hero with a wink, as he replied to her question. The answer she got was : ' Well, it's very kind of you to inquire, lady, but unless you're married I don't think I'd better tell you.' "

" Do you remember what an infernal nuisance the amateur strategist at the club became during the war, Alf ? "

" Do I not, old boy ! At first I used to think they were lots of fun, but, Lord, later how they bored one. They used to rush at a map like a bricklayer screaming for a quartern pot after eating salt fish."

" The alarmist newsmonger was a bright lad, too," said Edward, " and had ample scope when the Censor had not been over generous.

" What he didn't know about the Russians, for instance, was nobody's business. They were supposed to have been pouring through Great Britain for days. Eighty train-loads nightly from Leith—with blinds drawn and drums muffled. He had not seen them himself, he said, but his valet, whose brother was a gardener at York, was married to a girl whose uncle was a fisherman at Rosyth, had heard from a man who earned a living oyster shooting in the Hebrides, that ' he had seen the transports conveying our allies twice a week regularly to a place he was not allowed to mention.' "

" Oh, yes, that, dear fellow, was one of the best Cunards of the war, wasn't it ? "

" Of course, the most authentic story of the Russian troop trains was told by a Clapham man," said Alf, " who on arriving home after his day's work, informed his family that, although at first sceptical of the Cossacks' arrival in England, his doubts were now completely set at rest, as he had inspected a train in which he had been told they had travelled on the day before and had found the seats of the carriages all covered with snow."

"Yes, it certainly was all most amusing. People were so strung up they were ready to believe anything. You know, Alf, I think that almost as objectionable as the alarmist class of ass were the jokers whose witticisms, in such times as we were going through, were as jarring to the nerves of all thinking men as the sound of a step-dancer's shoes pattering on a coffin lid.

"You know the sort of funny man I mean, the gentleman who asked conundrums while the tape was spelling out relentlessly the names of men who were missing. This owl generally opened the ball with such questions as :

"'Why are fat women the bravest? Don't know? Why, because they are all out at the front.' Or, 'Have you heard that a spy was caught in Buckingham Palace to-night? Yes, really, in the billiard-room making cannons!'"

After having laughed over many similar little happenings, the two inseparables fell to remembering the recruiting stories, true or invented, which had amused the town twenty or more years ago.

Edward reminded his friend of one of the funniest of a large collection.

It was at the time when in London alone eight thousand men a day were joining up, that a man of sallow complexion and blue-black hair fell into a long line of splendid fellows who were flocking to the King's call.

After waiting for a couple of hours, his turn came at last

and he was asked various questions, which he answered only by violent gesticulations. Supposing him to be insane, the presiding medical officer ordered him to be locked up in one of the offices until such time as he could manage to interrogate him more fully. By some mischance the swarthy fellow was forgotten, and was not discovered till the following morning at nine o'clock. He turned out to be a Spaniard.

An interpreter was sent for, and to everyone's horror and surprise this subject of Europe's most sporting King proved to be a visitor to London on pleasure bent, who the day before had mistaken the waiting line of men enlisting for the queue of a cinema house; supposing that he was going to see Charlie Chaplin on a film, he had lost his temper, because, on demanding a seat, he had had all his clothes taken off and was most intensively examined—medically.

"I knew a small part actor," said Alf, "in a London theatre, who became a special constable, but threw it up in disgust, for I may say I think a very good and sufficient reason. It was this: 'You see, dear boy,' he said, 'they put me on night duty from ten till six in the morning. It was pouring with rain. I caught a shocking cold. I arrived home at seven—my wife thought I had been out with a lady and hasn't spoken to me since. I went to bed, over-slept myself, turned up late for rehearsal next morning, and was given the sack. No more Special Constabling for me, thank you.'"

"I think he was quite right, Alf."

"So do I, old man, and equally amusing when he gave his reasons for not enlisting. He said he knew what going to France would mean—getting sent into the firing line first pop off, being shot through the stomach, dying without

a round of applause, and having his name spelt wrong in
*The Era*."

For the benefit of the uninitiated, *The Era* is a well-known
theatrical newspaper which, years ago, was christened by
some wag " The Chorus Girls' Bible."

Many were the stories Damon and his friend remembered
of Kitchener.  One of two anecdotes, both of which were
probably quite untrue, but typical of the man who allowed
no one to take a liberty with him, was told about a very
distant relative of the distinguished soldier, who had been
given a minor staff appointment.  He was sent for by K.
of K. to receive orders before proceeding to Sir John French's
headquarters.  His Lordship gave the potential general his
commands, who, after listening attentively, nodded, saying
casually, " Righto, I understand," and turned to leave.

Kitchener waited until his cousin, nine times removed, had
reached the door, when he called out to him : " Oh, by the
way, next time call me Herbert ; it sounds more friendly ! "

" It's an odd thing," continued Alf, feeling in his pocket,
" but turning over some old New York papers this evening
before coming out, I came across this.

" It gave me a good laugh years ago.  It may not, dear
Edward, seem so funny as it did then.  After all, Time is
the only frame for a topical jest.  Still," he went on, " it's
worth having a look at, if only to make one remember the
All Highest at his lowest," and he tossed a cutting across the
table, which Edward picked up and read aloud.

### THE NEW TERROR
#### A Krupp Marvel

*New York, January 9th,* 1915 (via Lieville  Wireless).—It
appears that Herr von Krupp has had a new gun up his sleeve
that will strike horror into the hearts of the Allies, and will

end the war at the first shot. This gun weighs 27,000,000 tons, and the muzzle is so large that the Kaiser drove his limousine down the barrel. A troop of artillery went through, and a Zeppelin also flew down the gun from one end to the other. It fires a projectile that weighs 23,000,000 tons. On the projectile is a clock, and it also carries a time-table. It will be fired from Berlin at 9 a.m. and will destroy the following cities at the times mentioned :

|  | | | | | TIME |
|---|---|---|---|---|---|
| Leave Berlin, Germany | - | - | - | - | 9.0 a.m. |
| Arrive London, England | - | - | - | - | 9.1 a.m. |
| Arrive Paris, France | - | - | - | - | 9.2 a.m. |
| Arrive Sydney, Australia | - | - | - | - | 9.3 a.m. |
| Arrive British South Africa | - | - | - | - | 9.4 a.m. |
| Arrive Petrograd, Russia | - | - | - | - | 9.5 a.m. |
| Arrive Antwerp, Belgium | - | - | - | - | 9.6 a.m. |
| Arrive Ottawa, Canada | - | - | - | - | 9.7 a.m. |

The projectile is so highly trained that as it passes Ottawa and destroys the town, it picks up the Bank of England's 100,000,000 dollars gold reserve resting there, and flies back to Germany, landing it in the vaults of the Deutsche Bankgesell-schaft at 9.13 a.m.

A. D. LIARSBERG.

" The foregoing details," the comment says, " regarding the new Krupp Gun are confirmed by Count von Bernstorff, who stands ready to confirm anything favourable to Germany. ' I have known about this gun all along,' said the Count, ' but decided to keep it quiet. It was invented by Herr Krupp while playing a game of tennis with the Kaiser.' "

" Not bad, eh ? " laughed Alf.

" No, quite a good travesty in the best American style of the War Lord's attempt to frighten all and sundry at any price. What a hound ! Insane, do you suppose ? " asked Edward.

" Read Ludwig's book. He expresses no opinion. He leaves you to draw your own conclusions."

" And what were yours ? "

" Why, that he was mad, of course. ' Sent into this breathing world scarce half made up,' as Willie Shakespeare described Richard Three."

" Yes. I hope you will agree with me, Alf, old man," said Edward, " when I deliver myself of the following. All Dictators should be watched extremely carefully and on the first sign of their using the power they have seized for any purpose other than keeping their own house in order, they should be instantly put out of the way."

" I agree," said Alf. " In fact, if Dictators were real patriots they would put on their personal staff a minister who was an unerring shot and who should be given this order by the said Dictator himself : ' Sir, if you see me embarking on a policy which might create a war of any kind, you will know that I am insane and so you will immediately blow out my diseased brains over my nearest " yes man." I decorate you now for what I am about to receive and for which the world will be truly thankful.' "

" I suppose few will dispute the fact that with the exception of Foch the war produced no really outstanding military genius—anyone in the Napoleonic class, I mean," challenged Alf.

" My dear old man," bleated the humble one, " that of course *is* so, but if I may be permitted to express an opinion, you are wrong when you import the Napoleonic phrase. Master Bonaparte, with his rapid decisions, his cleavage of opposing forces and his lightning-like smashing of a left wing after having completely pulverised his enemies' right, would probably have been just at much as sea in 1914 as were his opponents in 1810.

" Fronts of hundreds of miles, and armies whose numbers

ran into millions, made it obviously impossible for any one man to gather what was happening everywhere, much less control far distant operations. No, Napoleon was a master in the days of miniature warfare, but a panorama cloth encompassing half the world would have no more been his game, I expect, than that of the many moderns who turned out to be brave but only brilliantly inadequate.

"In fact, I think the schoolboy's answer, when he was asked what he thought Napoleon would have done in the Great War was a classic reply to an impossible question. He very simply replied, 'Not much. He would have been too old!'"

"Not being a soldier," said Alf, "and never having had the slightest ambition to be dressed up in comic clothes and shout equally comic orders to my fellow creatures who are taught to become even more supremely ridiculous than Nature intended, by being drilled to look exactly like their not over individualistic next-door neighbour, I do not venture to express any opinion as to the merits of those who in a great gamble are encouraged to use men's lives as counters while they themselves blunder on through failure into very doubtful success."

"My dear old fellow, you expressed an opinion. I didn't attempt to answer it as I, too, have no knowledge of the gentle art of killing."

"Well, then, if we leave the great soldiers to rest on their laurels, or even on some one else's rhododendrons, for war is a disgusting and savage business which even the inmates of padded rooms would be ashamed to indulge in, what of the other figures—the political figures?"

"You are thinking of the chessmen, Alf?"

"Yes."

# TWO MEN TALK

" I never played the game," said Edward. " In politics this is by no means necessary," Alf observed.

" What I mean, my dear Edward, is, can you recall anyone in particular who as a figure stood out as a great memory to you ? I can."

" You mean above all others ? "

" Yes, I don't mean immeasurably superior to all others, as it would be quite impossible to pick out any dozen people, let alone one man, from the host of mighty men such as Northcliffe, Lloyd George, Baldwin, Asquith, and many others who loomed large on Britain's horizon in those days that had their birth in Belgium.

" I was thinking more of a man on an occasion. It was Winston Churchill, when he announced to an astonished London what the war looked like demanding in man power from England. Perhaps he made such an indelible impression on my mind because of the sudden and staggering surprise he sprang upon his listeners."

" Where did you hear him, Alf ? "

" At the Stoll Picture Palace. In those days it was Hammerstein's Opera House."

" Hammerstein, who was he ? "

" A German called Murphy from Chicago, I think" said Alf. " It was a relation of his, I believe, who not long ago came to London with a little group of similar Scotch Americans and decided that Drury Lane should be turned into a thoroughly National Theatre by importing the best Broadway musical plays the United States had to offer."

" Fancy such a thing being possible," said Edward incredulously.

" You may well say that, Edward, my boy. Indeed, I

often think that many of our British shareholders are half witted."

"They would be if they had a little more brains," smiled Edward. "But go on, let us hear about Winston."

"Well, I had always been one of Churchill's greatest admirers, and it was strange for me to see for the first time in the flesh a man whom I had only known through photographs and caricatures."

"Which did he look like most ? " queried Edward.

Alf took no notice of the interruption and proceeded as if he were talking to himself.

"I arrived late, I remember, just as Churchill was about to commence his speech. He was not at all as I had imagined him. He began to speak in a high-pitched squeaky voice —with his hands holding the lapels of his frock-coat somewhat high up—the reason for this being, as I afterwards discovered, that they had not in them the breadth of gesture associated with the professional flinger of oratorical blossoms. I watched him very earnestly for a few minutes and found myself in the presence of a great and dominant personality. I admired him none the less that at first it was to me by no means a fascinating one.

"I very quickly felt I was watching, and I say it with profound respect, a strangely brave and undefeatable animal.

"His rounded shoulders which supported a head that looked too big for the body it governed, his sandy colouring his eyes that as he spoke became invisible, and his tongue which seemed to hiss savagely against his eye teeth, conveyed, to me nothing so much as a red weasel who, having settled on the back of a rabbit, was steadily biting his way into its skull, and that rabbit was Germany.

"He spoke deliberately, the sentences being carefully chosen

as such an occasion demanded. One or two admirable
phrases raised a storm of cheering, such as his witty description of the North Sea, as ' the so-called German Ocean,'
and a hope that the Kaiser would soon find out that the
reason the bulldog's nose slanted backwards was that it
enabled him to breathe when once he got hold.

" The speech for the most part was plain statement of fact,
trenchantly delivered with every considered point wonderfully made in level tones, though when the voice *was* raised
it was for a very well thought out effect.

" Of flashing oratory there was none. The little figure
handicapped as it was by a poor delivery and poorer gestures,
held the vast audience spellbound. They were listening to
the first story of the war from the man who had known
of its coming and who had been ready when it
came.

" War had been thrust upon us, and Churchill had put
the Navy to sea like a flash, complete and stronger than
it had ever been before in the history of the Empire."

" Yes, my hat, I remember that, Alf."

" What a performance ! So it was not to be wondered
at that even the political opponents who listened to him
did so with a lump in their throats and hands ready to
applaud his slightest hesitation."

" I wonder what this genius is like in private life, old
man ? "

" I don't know, Edward. I wish I did. There's one
thing, however, I am certain of—that he is not only the
blood and bone of a patriotic Englishman, but he is a
mighty showman who knows every trick of the trade, from
the encouraging of age to sit upon unnecessarily stooping
shoulders to the manipulation of a pair of white delicate-

looking hands which attract the eye, being as they are the outposts of a great brain.

"Few men could have made so grave a pronouncement as he did without causing panic—it was that '*next spring we should have one million picked troops in the field.*' But this he did and in such a wonderful way that the House rose at him, and I think had he said *two* millions, the cheers would have been even louder.

"A great Englishman was the man I saw, and not one of the least of the effects he made upon me, when he sat down at the end of his effort, was the glance he cast with a half-inquiring smile at a box on the second tier, to a beautiful lady, who must have been as proud of her husband as was the vast audience he had swept off its feet.

"How weary and heart-sick one became of the whole ghastly business," were Edward's spoken thoughts. "On and on it dragged, success followed by disaster—optimistic reports and hopes dashed, casualty lists yards long, and nearly all one's middle-aged friends in mourning for their sons, with the end never in sight."

"I shall never forget," answered Alf, "a splendid idiot wandering into the club towards the end of the third year of Armageddon and remarking profoundly that he had no idea when the war would end, to which a wit replied, 'Really? I cannot help feeling that your ignorance is assumed.'

"It was this same humorist, who, when he heard that armistice had come, remarked dryly, 'Ah, well, this will stimulate recruiting.'

"Do you remember some of the magnificent music-hall drivel which was sung at the time—stuff which might have prompted our old friend Dogberry to have written down the authors as asses, but was cheered to the echo by the crowd. The song which lived in my memory as an expression of good honest unsophisticated tripe was that lyrical expression of massed patriotism entitled ' *FIRE !* ' I have never forgotten it ; this is it :

> " F—I—R—E—Fire,
> See the flames mount 'igher and 'igher,
> F stands for France,
> I for h'Italy,
> R stands for Russia,
> But what about the E ?
> E stands for dear old England,
> Of that we make no doubt,
> So if we pull together,
> And fight 'em 'ell for leather,
> We're sure to put the fire out.

" This was the chorus handed out to vast audiences by a lovely lady in tights, who encouraged them to shout it back at her whole-heartedly. Mind you," continued Alf, " it may have been crude, but it must not be wiped off the slate as of no value whatever. It was the only expression of the will to win known to the masses."

" Oh, I quite agree," said Edward, " but one can't help being struck with the fact that in the short space of twenty years times have so changed that if war broke out to-day no one in this country would listen to that sort of jingo stuff, let alone sing it."

" You may be right, old man, but what you are saying now was said when King Edward came to the throne, and you couldn't have had any greater nonsense than some of the lyrical efforts with war as their subject which were popular in his reign, and yet fifteen years later we sang together ' *FIRE !* ' "

" But surely, Alf, nothing quite so ridiculous as that ? "

" Yes, just as banal, and really, in a way, worse, because take, for instance, that classic, ' There'll be no war.' This, you remember, was sung with immense pathos, and many were the tears shed in the halls by the unsophisticated, who felt it to be the real sob stuff."

" I've forgotten it, Alf."

" I never could, old boy. This is it," and Alf proceeded very slowly and with great feeling to ladle out softly the song that had reached the hearts of the mothers who loved their sons and had sublime faith in their King :

> " There'll be no war,
>    As long as there's a King like good King Edward,
> There'll be no war,
>    He hates that kind of thing.

> " Mothers don't worry,
>    As long as there's a King like good King Edward.
> Peace and Honour is the motto that he loves,
>    So God bless our King."

As he finished he looked up and saw that three waiters who had listened to his crooning were crying salt tears into the dishes they carried. The customers who had ordered them inquired of the *maître d'hôtel* if the chef was on intimate terms with Lot's wife.

# PART II

## Famous Ladies of the Stage

At whatever hour Alf stepped, stumbled or fell into bed, his servant always called him at seven and presented him with his letters, nearly all of which contained that opening sentence known to so many of us, "Dear Sir, We are surprised."

Why West End tradesmen were ever surprised had from time immemorial surprised Alf.

His breakfast invariably consisted of three cups of tea and half a piece of toast, which he munched after he had given, as he called it, his morning concert, which was an obbligato conducted by Monsieur Martell, whom he made a point of meeting every evening, and who had trained his vocal chords to give a delightful rendering of that popular potpourri entitled "Spiritland," which is the signature tune of every gentleman of leisure.

Having devoured with his tea and toast the contents of a dozen morning papers, so as to become *au fait* with the views of other scribes before arriving at the office of the newspaper wherein he prostituted his brains for bread and butter, he opened a letter from his Editor.

It appeared that a colleague of his, whose usual job was to review books, had been sent away to write about the Navy, and his Chief wished him to look through some six or seven new works which needed man-handling. Among these he noticed one devoted to Tabloid Biographies of Famous Ladies of the Stage.

It was written by some one who had elected to conceal his identity by calling himself " Semorix."

Being slightly intrigued, as the title seemed to open up various possibilities, he chose it for his dissecting room to see what its author had to say about such well-known folk as Madame Nellie Melba, Gracie Fields, Ellaline Terriss, Gladys Cooper, Lady Tree, Yvonne Printemps and many another famous favourite of to-day and yesterday.

Perhaps he would find, he thought, nothing he was not well aware of and little that was new, but on the other hand he might have his memory pleasantly refreshed. So leaving the best sellers to their fate, he proceeded idly to turn the pages of a work which, if not illuminating, would, he hoped, possess much of the genteel feeling attributed to the immortal Bob Acres.

The tome was dedicated to some lady who had evidently annoyed the author ; it ran :

> " To a beautiful woman whom I thought I knew,
> How good, how true, how wonderful she wasn't."

The first chapter was headed " Melba," and Alf, having known the great singer personally, became mildly interested.

It commenced :

A wag of a scribe once replied to his editor on being asked by him to write a set of Tabloid Biographies, giving intimate glimpses of well-known people, that he would rather not do so, as to tell the real truth about the famous would be either to make them delightfully infamous or duller than ditch-water, before he had spoiled a single page of his precious paper. I, however, do not share this merry fellow's opinion. This may be, of course, because on glancing at the list of ladies I have been bidden to remember, no single one could possibly be anything but " Pretty Thoughts " from the borders of Lavender, which trim the paths they have trodden in a garden which has " Rosemary " written across its lichen-covered gate.

As I sit wondering with whom and how to begin this series of reminiscences of famous ladies, my eye lights upon a treasured picture on which is written " With love from Nellie Melba "; so, as this is surely the voice of an old friend calling, why should I not commence with one who linked with Adelina Patti as Patti linked with Jenny Lind— a century of song.

Singers ? I have met very few. I was almost going to say " Thank the Lord," for the ladies who imagine that they presented the Almighty with the vocal chords which have earned them fame and also are sure they explained to the Deity exactly where they wished them placed, are, as a rule, a pest, possessed of nothing but airs and anything but graces. However, one superlative artist I did know very well, over a period of some five and thirty years. This was Melba! and mighty singer though she was, never in private life was she other than a very direct and down-to-earth lady. She was possessed of a dominant personality, one which I fancy inspired admiration and respect, but seldom spontaneous affection, from those with whom she came in contact. Indeed, I think she rather made those about her fearful of her displeasure, for she was intolerant of ordinary people, and was the last person to brook opposition, even over the most trivial matters.

In speaking of her like this I must not be accused of condemning her in private life ; on the contrary, considering that she for many years had the world at her feet and was fawned upon, not only by the public, but by kings and princes, it is very wonderful that she should not have become absolutely intolerable ; but, though difficult, she was to be forgiven and in a sense applauded, for she was not only crowned by the world " Queen of Song," but had crowned herself the legitimate Queen over everyone who challenged her supremacy on the operatic stage.

Her acting was poor, but her technique as a singer beyond words marvellous, for even as an old woman, when the Voice had waned with the years, she could hold vast audiences spellbound with the magic of her knowledge of the art in which she had been pre-eminent.

I heard her in *Bohème* at her farewell performance in Melbourne, a ghost of her great self, but still a giant. Her series of farewells was considered a thing to jest about. But why? She was clever enough to know that with her technique alone she still held all comers at bay, and although Shakespeare himself wrote that farewell was easily said, I beg to differ, for "Farewell!" is, I think, the saddest word in our beautiful language.

Operatic artists are known to be the most jealous people in the world, and Melba was no exception, for I well remember her undisguised annoyance at the advent on her horizon of Tetrazzini. It was at a supper party she gave, while singing in the Isle of Man, that on some one mentioning Tetrazzini's recent triumph in London, not only did she explode verbally, but even went to the length of rising from the table and prancing about, saying, "This is what Tetrazzini will do, no doubt, if she sings on horseback, and this" (making snorting noises) "is what I suppose the poor horse will do which is obliged to carry her."

For an artist in her zenith—I speak of forty years ago—such a performance seemed to me incredibly petty, and yet, might she not have thought that her citadel was being stormed and suddenly have developed an inferiority complex? If this were so she was to be forgiven, for surely greatness must always be looked upon with a kindly and forgiving eye.

In thinking of the difficult times managers have with the majority of people in opera, I remember once Sir Augustus Harris (known to the London of his day as Druriolanus) saying that the only way he was able to conciliate various stars when travelling together, if he was obliged to place one great singer over the other in the sleeping berths, was to have a placard with "and" placed between them, so that the lady in the lower bunk would feel that she was on perfectly equal terms artistically with her sister who slumbered overhead.

As a business woman, Melba had the brain of a business man and saw life through the spectacles of her Scottish ancestors. Of gentleness she had little, of humour none. Her fun was the obvious, and commanding as she did the applause courtiers are trained to give to Royalty for the most futile of sallies, she was mercifully unaware that had she not been Melba, a yawn would have replaced the ever-ready guffaw.

To me she was always extraordinarily kind and, although I can say I was never easy in her presence, I was fond of her, though frightened of her moods, which found birth in a quick mentality always just ahead of the moment.

I have said there was little gentleness about her, but there I was wrong, for the face which was hard and by no means beautiful, softened beyond measure as she played with her little grand-daughter (now grown into a charming young lady), for whom, I remember, she took delight in watching as the child played with a lamb she had bought for her in Melbourne, and which she had brought back in triumph to her lovely home, called " Lillydale," some five and twenty miles from that entrancing city.

Her jewels were marvellous and her cabinets were filled with wonders of the goldsmith's art, all of them presentations from the most noble and the most famous of every land she had enthralled with her God-given voice. The one story she loved to tell against herself was that of a gentleman on board a P. & O. liner bound for Australia.

This worthy, quite unaware that the one and only Melba was on board, was splashing about in his bath the first day out at sea, and, hearing some one singing in the next cabin, shouted out : " Oh, for heaven's sake shut up ! " His consternation may well be imagined when later in the afternoon it was made known to him that the voice belonged to a lady who would have probably charged him a thousand guineas had he engaged her to sing at his private house, and that only *if* she could have been persuaded to do so.

Melba was often very pleased with simple things, although accustomed to the best the world could offer, and I remember once she seemed more than delighted with a dedication I wrote to her in a little book called "Hullo, Australia!" We were sitting at a restaurant in Sydney, when she suddenly said, "I hear you are writing a book about my country. Is that so?" When I replied that it was true and that I was dedicating it to her, she became greatly interested, and asked what form the dedication was to take. Frankly, I had not thought of it, but I scribbled on the back of the luncheon menu a line which I think gave her pleasure. It was: "The voice of a nightingale was hushed when Melba sang."

In his early days Landon (now Sir Landon) Ronald was invariably her accompanist at the piano, and while he always addressed her as "Queen," she took a delight in teasing him about his nose, which is, as he himself often remarks, an outside size in noses. She would chaff him unmercifully, a thing which this great musician and charming gentleman always took in very good part. It was while at Douglas, Isle of Man, that on my asking Landon to come out with me for the afternoon, he replied: "Well, yes, I will, I have nothing particular to do here, except to look after Melba." His reply called forth a yell of laughter from the assembled company, all of whom knew the *diva* and were well aware that to look after her and obey her commands was very nearly a three-man job.

It was Melba, who discovered the genius of that great throat specialist, Sir Milsom Rees, and I think she was never happy unless he was within call, for he understood her delicate and sensitive vocal organs as no other man ever did. Never shall I forget going with her to a throat doctor in a great northern city, for she made the poor man, metaphorically, sink through the floor. She had caught a slight cold and after this good gentleman had examined her carefully, she inquired of him what he proposed to do. " Paint your throat with nitrate of silver," he replied. " What ? " she almost screamed, " paint my beautiful vocal chords with stuff of that kind ? You must be mad," and paying him his fee, she flounced out of the house like a whirlwind.

On her singing nights she whispered all day and, indeed, seldom spoke at all, so careful was she of the gifts she treasured. Why she was never waylaid at night-time on her motor ride from Sydney to her country house was a thing at which I have often marvelled, for unattended she would often carry with her the thousands and thousands of pounds' worth of jewellery she had worn at the theatre.

For a fellow countryman of hers, Haddon Chambers, she had the greatest admiration as an author, and was very fond of him as a man. She was not in London when this witty man of the world died, and when she inquired of me the details of his death and as to how he had succeeded in his later years, long after I had finished telling her all I could about our mutual friend, she sat silent, looking through the rose-covered pergolas of her lovely garden out into the bluest of blue Australian skies, so far removed from the drab streets of our great metropolis which surrounded an opera house in Covent Garden to which Haddon, in company with many another of her devoted friends, had so often accompanied her.

Not the least of Melba's many great qualities was the staunch way, come good or ill, she stood by those of whom she was fond. Socially, of course, she was big enough to do this, but there are many who would have hesitated to stand by some unfortunate, whom the world refused to pardon. The great singer was a big-hearted human being, who felt that a sin atoned for should not be made punishable for ever.

Talking of punishment, it was Charles Brookfield, one of the most acid of Victorian wits, who meeting, in the Haymarket, a friend who had just served a sentence of five years' penal servitude, greeted him with great cordiality.

The sinner, taken aback, expecting no doubt to be deliberately cut, said to Brookfield, " Thank you very much, my dear fellow ; I thought you would pass me by."

" On the contrary," said Brookfield, " I thought you would pass me by. You see you've done your time, I haven't done mine."

It is sad to think I shall never meet Melba again, and on returning to Australia, as I hope to some day, it will be, I fear, like wandering through a beautiful garden, straining my ears in vain to hear an echo of the lovely voice the angels have welcomed to their choir.

Alf had not read the first paragraph of the chapter devoted to Gladys Cooper before he discovered that Semorix was the *nom de plume* of a very old friend of his, an actor who has painted his nose for the public's annoyance night after night over a period of fifty years. He was not quite sure if friendship like absence should make the heart grow fonder, but he did feel that if a bludgeon should be deserved he could perhaps be lenient and use a cane rather than the heavier weapon, without in any way feeling that he had failed in his duty as a critic.

# GLADYS COOPER

My first memory of this beautiful woman was seeing her, as almost a child, sitting in the Savoy Grillroom at a time when she was rehearsing to play, with a provincial company, the part of Bluebell in a play I wrote called " Bluebell in Fairyland." I did not speak to her.

Some years later I happened to visit the Gaiety Theatre to see a Musical Comedy called " The Girls of Gothenburg," and, singing in a sextet (which had for its refrain the extremely brainy words, " Hulloa People, People Hulloa ! "), to my surprise I saw the Bluebell of a few summers before. What her capabilities as an actress might be I hadn't the faintest idea, but, with such a face, I knew, if she couldn't do something, she would have to be stupid to the last degree, and as this I was quite sure was most improbable, I wrote to her and asked her to come and see me.

Being under no definite contract to the Gaiety management, and having little chance of getting on in a Musical Comedy house, being neither a singer nor a dancer, she accepted a three years' contract with me and, after a very short period, became my leading lady for several seasons, playing in sketches at the Coliseum and the provincial Music Halls and also creating the part of the heroine in George M. Cohan's amusing piece, " Broadway Jones."

Appreciative though I was of her talents and hard work, never did I suspect that playing with me was some one who would turn out to be an actress of great outstanding merit, and who, indeed, to my mind, was the most wonderful Mrs. Tanqueray I ever saw. Comparisons, as Mrs. Candour remarked, are at all times odorous, but giving in, even Mrs. Campbell and Mrs. Kendal (who played the part in New York and brought to the character every weapon in her marvellous armoury), Gladys Cooper gave to Mrs. Tanqueray something that made Pinero's thirty-year-old dialogue sound as if it had been written only the day before.

We worked together, off and on, from the end of 1911 till the end of 1914, and it has been a delight to me to see this exceptional person, who began her career with me, place her banner unaided upon the topmost heights.

Thinking of 1914, Gladys Cooper, in company with Ellaline Terriss and Ivy St. Helier, was one of the first actresses to go to the Front, there to help cheer the brave men who, under Sir John French, were fighting for our safety and their very existence. It was during the performance we gave behind the lines that, listening to Miss Cooper recite Kipling's " Gunga Din," I became aware of a depth of power within her which she had never hitherto had an opportunity of showing while appearing in the trivial comedies in which she had started to make a name.

That awful Christmas of '14 in France was bitterly cold, and it was with the greatest admiration I watched the untiring and successful efforts of these three popular ladies to bring a breath of home to the wounded and mud-covered men returning to the rest camps from the trenches. If it may be of interest to my readers to see the programme given by the first troupe of British players who tried to do their little bit during those terrible and, pray God, never-to-be-repeated times ; here it is :

# NIGHT LIGHTS

## THE NATIONAL THEATRE AT "THE FRONT"

A TENT—A ROADSIDE—A HOSPITAL—ANYWHERE.
SOLDIERS,

Fellow-countrymen of whom we are so proud, and to whom we owe so much.

*By permission of*
FIELD-MARSHAL EARL KITCHENER OF KHARTOUM,
O.M., G.S.C.I., etc., Secretary of State for War,

and with the approval of

FIELD-MARSHAL SIR JOHN FRENCH, O.M., K.C.M.G., etc.,
Commander-in-Chief of the British Expeditionary Forces

*We, your brothers and sisters, have come over from England to try and entertain and amuse you during New Year's week and to bring you*

### "A MESSAGE FROM HOME."

*You have only to command us, and we shall be proud to give you the best entertainment in our power*

AT ANY TIME AND AT ANY PLACE.

ELLALINE TERRISS will sing more sweetly and act more charmingly than ever for you.

SEYMOUR HICKS will perspire more freely.

BEN DAVIES will sing as he never sang before.

GLADYS COOPER will act and look more like her postcards than she does.

IVY ST. HELIER will delight you as she has always done.

WILLIE FRAME will make you laugh as much in France as he does in Bonnie Scotland. Och Hi!

WILL VAN ALLEN will patter and play all day.

ELI and OLGA HUDSON. Well! you know how you love to hear them.

THE CINEMATOGRAPH will show you thousands of feet of amusing films.

# FAMOUS LADIES OF THE STAGE

COME IN, SOLDIERS,

AS MANY OF YOU AND OFTEN AS YOU LIKE.

*You will confer a favour on us by letting us work for you, and the angels in disguise, the brave ladies who nurse you, ask them to honour us with their presence also.*

## GOD SAVE THE KING !

GOD PROTECT YOU AND YOUR BRAVE ALLIES.

VIVE LA FRANCE AND BRAVO, BRAVE BELGIUM !

LONG LIVE ENGLAND !

THE PRICE OF ADMISSION IS : OUR GRATITUDE TO YOU.

Alas ! dear old Willie Frame, who was then over seventy, is no more, and Eli Hudson, one of the greatest flautists of his day, joining up later, succumbed to the hardships which he, with a million others, endured. But that beautiful singer and gallant gentleman, Ben Davies, is still with us and even to-day, at an age of which he is justly proud, still holds spellbound with his matchless technique those who are privileged to hear him sing, " To Mary," " Araby," and the innumerable songs which he has made famous and with which he has enthralled the multitude.

But to return to Gladys Cooper, a thing which everyone who knows her is ever eager to do. Any star with less " side " on than she has I think it would be difficult to find, and her pretty ears must often burn—if ears really do burn —when the world says nothing but nice things about those who own these ridiculous Mickey Mouse appendages.

In a book she wrote, she described me as a man who " had made more women cry and more men swear than anyone on the stage." This being quite untrue, though I do not deny that I am a trifle difficult at times, I very naturally wondered somewhat, until I discovered that words let fall by her carelessly about an old friend, being a bit trying in the theatre, had been exaggerated by a professional scribe who had assisted her in the compiling of a classic.

As a companion she is delightful, for her sense of humour is a thing that all women may well envy, and as a business woman she is not only splendid, but can take the rough with the smooth under any circumstances, as few in our precarious profession have been able to.

I do not know her handicap at golf, but, whether it be high or low, this I am well aware of, that, in everything else she turns her hand to, she is certainly among those who, starting from scratch, win easily.

Looking at her to-day, with her girlish figure, it seems difficult to believe that she is the mother of a grown-up son and of two daughters. Indeed, were it not that her boy John is at the moment acting splendidly, I should say it was an impossibility. But there it is. Time does fidget, as a celebrated burlesque writer once informed us, and alas ! the years gallop faster than the greatest racing certainty ever known. So fast indeed, that though Gladys Cooper used to play opposite me on to-be-excused stage terms, for I was many years her senior, to-day, if I acted with her, I should have to cast myself for the part, not of her one-time histrionic admirer, but most probably that of a doting father.

Alf had known well and greatly admired the perfect type of English beauty he had just read about and indeed had been one of her first husband's oldest friends. The ever-popular " Buck," who knows more people and more about people than probably all the members of his famous club put together.

A witty and amusing fellow is Buck, with whom Alf had

FIRST CONCERT PARTY TAKEN OUT TO FRANCE, DECEMBER, 1914.

supped only a few nights before and had listened to him keep the company in high good humour with one of his remarks which was anything but second-class; this was a reply to a youth who had been landed with a breach of promise case. "Ah!" said Buck, "take a woman on your knee and she'll sit on you for ever." While to a friend who in triumph declared that after months of pursuit he had at length persuaded the lady he was in love with to look upon him with a kindly eye, he said, "Go and send a telegram to yourself, dear fellow, just saying, 'At long lust.'"

# ELLEN TERRY

When she was born a star danced.

Sad it may be that we have lost the manners of a pre-war period, but sadder still am I for those who never saw the elfin greatness of this divine actress, who illuminated every scene in which she appeared, bringing the joy of life on to the stage and, like a sunbeam, flooded the auditorium, making its lamps burn blue for very shame.

Wayward, inconsequent, affectionate and vital, it can be truly said that she was worshipped by every playgoer in the land, and that in her private life she had not an enemy in the world. Oh! what a delicate, lovely, sensitive face was hers! What poise! and what gesture! What technical skill in the handling of flowing draperies and what a carriage was hers as she moved to the music of the poet's verse!

Never shall we see her like again, or a partnership to be compared with those great Lyceum days when she and the mighty Irving, high above their fellows, looked down upon the pygmies who toiled in their art so far beneath.

Ellen to the public, she was Nell to her friends, and, indeed, was as child-like a little Nell by nature, in her old age, as she was when she made her first appearance at the Princess's Theatre, playing Puck, at the age of eight, in Charles Kean's production of " A Midsummer Night's Dream."

I possessed the first playbill on which her name appeared, but it was stolen from me by some kindly enthusiast, maybe the same gentleman who absent-mindedly appropriated the prayer book which Henry Irving held in his hands as Becket on the night of his death. I wish he would return these treasures !

The life slogan of Ellen Terry was " Work is Worship," and this will be found above her name in many a thousand autograph books. Henry Irving, self-centred to a degree, a man who was seldom, if ever, to be seen in the company of ladies, adored his helpmate in art and gave her as a woman the unbounded affection that loving fathers give their favourite daughter. Indeed, whenever in doubt or quandary, " Nell " went to " Henry " to unravel the problem, a thing he always did with that gentle and old-world charm of manner of which Nature had robbed a multitude to bestow on him.

I remember once sitting in the great actress's drawing-room at Barkiston Gardens, hearing her railing at the notices of her performance in a new producton. They were all wonderful, but what she took exception to was the fact that nearly every critic referred to the " Terry charm." She threw away the cuttings with a merry laugh, saying, " Oh ! how sick I am of this charm business. I wish I'd never had any," and then continued, " Anyhow, I don't believe I have any charm, so they're all of them wrong." Had she been able to see herself at that very moment, she would have known that she indeed was charm itself. Many a critic dwelt continually on this valuable asset of hers, and, in doing so, sometimes forgot that beneath an apparently unconscious fairy-like performance in comedy, she was possessed of magical technique, equal, indeed, to that of her superlative rival, Madge Kendal, the greatest all-round actress I ever saw.

What a sense of fun had Ellen Terry ; an infectious gaiety was hers, as she trod on air, fluttering like some lovely butterfly from flower to flower, even when skies were overcast. A minor poet of her day, one Alfred Calmour, who wrote the "Amber Heart," in which she appeared, at one period of their friendship took umbrage at some trivial happening and, sulking in that corner which is reserved for poets, wrote her a letter which commenced with the words, "My dear Miss Terry, the *dear* is purely conventional," to which our Nell replied, "My dear Mr. Calmour, the *dear* is purely theatrical."

To those who at first may not understand this to be a witty rejoinder, may I explain that the word "dear" in the world of the Theatre is quite meaningless, being used by artists to each other almost as they are introduced. To an author who had pestered her to read an extremely bad play, in returning it, not wishing to hurt his feelings, all she wrote was :

"Dear Mr. Chichester, I have read your play. Oh, my dear Mr. Chichester !—Yours, E. T."

On one occasion she lectured me very seriously for not having accepted an offer from Henry Irving to play the boy in "Robespierre," a very fine part which would have been, as she put it, a stepping stone to bigger things. When however, I explained my reasons for not coming to the Lyceum, she laughed, a laugh like the chiming of silver bells. My explanation was this : In trepidation I had gone to the first rehearsal of Sardou's drama. Peeping through the gloom of a curtained stage, I had seen Irving seated, to me a terrifying figure, instructing his actors, as was his habit, how to play their parts, even to the minutest detail. So frightened was I at the prospect of having to appear before him that, in panic, I slipped my manuscript into the prompter's hand and, running into the Strand, was lost for many days.

# FAMOUS LADIES OF THE STAGE

There was not the slightest reason I should have done this, for Irving was ever kindly to small people, and held the very decided view that, even at the age of seventy, we were all only children in Art.

I once heard Miss Terry, in speaking with her usual enthusiasm about her partner, deliver herself of an admirable mot : "Ah! how much more wonderful Henry is than any other I have ever seen, and when he retires the Stagg may fall on some one but never the Mantle." I suppose every one knows that Stagg & Mantle were a firm from which ladies could purchase all the things dear to their hearts.

Ellen Terry never suffered from being over-punctual, and often arrived at the Theatre giving herself barely time to dress and make up, and many a time she used almost to give the stage managers heart disease as she tripped into the wings at the last moment, adjusting the buttons of her dress as she walked into a scene of comedy or tragedy, to receive a mighty welcome from a crowded house.

In her zenith the hold she had upon the public was extraordinary. When Henry Irving was touring the United States and filling every theatre to capacity, Ellen Terry was taken ill during a season in Chicago and was obliged to go out of the bill. "Faust" was being played at the time, and although the production was stupendous, the receipts immediately dropped by nearly fifty per cent.

Her popularity was so great that, even when she forgot her words, which in later years was not infrequent, the audience loved her all the more. On one occasion I saw her in "The Merry Wives of Windsor" at His Majesty's Theatre, and when she peeped from under a table, and with a happy smile said, "Oh dear, I've forgotten what I have to say next!" the house shouted their loving forgiveness and devotion.

# NIGHT LIGHTS

Some few months before her death she did me the honour of coming to see me play at the Garrick Theatre. Much fuss was, of course, made of her, and I sent her my homage, with a large basket of fruit and flowers. At the end of the performance I ran round to see her safely out of the theatre, and, thanking me for the little offering, she said, " My dear, you must ask me to come and see you if ever you act in London." I often wondered if this was because she had really lost her memory, or that, playing as well as I could, I had made no impression on her whatever; perhaps this was so.

I saw her in almost every piece in which she appeared. My greatest regret is that she never played Rosalind, for she would have been the most, one might almost write, Impish Fairy in this Shakespearean fairy tale. Hers would not have been the flat-footed portrayal of this impossible lady so often to be seen nowadays. She would have danced through the home of the Banished Duke, bringing, as she teased her Orlando to the top of his bent, a fragrance across the footlights that would have made the bluebells and primroses, seeking sanctuary at the foot of the oaks beneath which Jacques soliloquised so wonderfully, green with envy.

Yes! A star danced when she was born. A total eclipse happened when a bell tolled for the passing of the greatest and most lovable Nell Theatre-land had ever known.

Alf had the misfortune of never having seen Ellen Terry except as an old lady playing old ladies' parts and therefore was delighted to take for granted the lines he had just read, and as on the next page he saw the name of the immortal Duse, he felt he was in exactly the same position, only having heard of this wonderful woman.

# ELEANORA DUSE

To write of the immortal Duse from an intimate point of view would be, except for an almost microscopical minority, an impossibility. No oyster lived within its shell in greater security than this heaven-born genius. For not only did she shun publicity of every kind, but few save those who were very close to her ever had an opportunity of meeting her in private, let alone obtaining a viewpoint from her of her art.

Still, it cannot be but of interest to every theatre lover to recall memories of one of the greatest actresses that ever stepped. Who of those who saw her will ever forget her " Camille," for instance, so unlike any other lady who wore the lovely white flowers after which Marguerite Gautier was play-named ?

Closing my eyes, I can see her now in the last act of that classic. How desperately ill was Camille, not dying as an actress, but dying indeed, with her head buried beneath the pillows, striving to shut out the world around her, praying for death to release her from the agony of lost love.

Hers was a beautiful face, sensitive to joy and sorrow, which were registered upon it so wonderfully that even those unable to understand the words she spoke, playing in Italian as she did, became perfectly aware of all that Duse was thinking. Her eyes were dark and luminous, her brows square and her mouth a drooping and tragic one.

Born amidst the humblest surroundings, she had known

the direst poverty in childhood, more often than not being without food. It is recorded that her mother, being in hospital, used to set aside a cup of soup, which was part of her diet, to give the little Eleanora on her daily visit to the ward in which she lay.

It is said that it was the hardships she endured in these early days which made her look sadly at life, even in the hours of phenomenal triumph, through eyes that had seen suffering from many a sorrowing angle.

May it not be, however, that these very privations which were hers were what gave to the world this wonderful woman? " She learned in suffering what they teach in song." She was often called the Ellen Terry of Italy, and it is strange that her friend Ellen Terry herself never tired of saying that " it is only through great suffering that one can become a great artist."

To discuss her methods from the point of view of art or heart, or art and heart, is not my province; for reams have been written on this subject in books and by critics. But one of the things which struck me most as I watched her continually was the beauty of her hands, which, like those of Lucien Guitry and Henry Irving, and indeed of every great actor, "*spoke*."

She appeared at Drury Lane on the occasion of Ellen Terry's Benefit, and, as I opened the performance on that historic afternoon by playing in a sketch with Ellaline Terriss, I can say—and do with pride—that I appeared on the same stage with her.

She delivered herself of many " wise saws and modern instances," as The Bard has put it, one being that " no one can *really* act more than once a week." What in 1938 would she say, I wonder, of the appalling twice-nightly rule, which is so often necessary in these days of competition, if our butchers and bakers and such like people are to be paid.

Of fads and foibles she had many, not the least of which was that when appearing in Ibsen's " Ghosts " she always insisted on having a cyclamen placed upon the stage.

In having remarked previously of the difficulty of obtaining an interview with her of any kind, the story is told of a journalist who even went to the length of obtaining a situation as a waiter in the hotel at which she was staying, so that he might obtain first-hand copy about her.

She made exceptions of no one. The story that she refused even kings an entrée to her dressing-room at the theatre was perfectly true—being adamant even on the night that the King of Wurtemburg sent his marshal saying that he would like to see her. To this gentleman of the Court Duse said, " Please thank His Majesty infinitely, but I only receive very intimate friends in my dressing-room." Later in the evening the King himself knocked at her door. She simply said, " Sire, I am dressing." His Majesty replied, " I will wait." She answered, " It is quite useless. I cannot break my rule, and pray your Majesty to pardon me."

The King of Sweden, however, gained admittance by more tactful and diplomatic methods. The message he sent Signora Duse was this : " Tell her it is not the king who seeks an audience ; it is the humblest of her subjects."

Her grandfather and father had both been struggling actors. It was that tremendous tragedian, Salvini, who, seeing her either in Verona, where she appeared as Juliet at the age of sixteen, or in Turin—I forget which—prophesied her ultimate triumphs.

It is said that she first saw the light of day in a railway carriage, and was such an abnormally small baby that she was carried to her christening in a tiny cradle, decorated with gold and crystals. On her way to the church, a company of soldiers, mistaking the little casket for one which contained some sacred relics, presented arms. This, as her father afterwards said, must surely be good augury for her future.

Eleanora Duse, whose life, from a domestic point of view, was one of sorrow and infinite pain, died of pneumonia in America.

At the announcement of her passing the world of the Theatre was stunned, and the playgoers who had worshipped in thousands at her feet, looked, hopelessly, into the darkness for some one to take her place. This was not to be.

" Ah ! Ha ! " said Alf to himself as he saw the name of Mrs. Patrick Campbell, " here is some one I do know and there is nothing I suppose my friend, who seems to amuse himself by writing in his spare time, can tell me and of which I am not fully aware."

# MRS. PATRICK CAMPBELL

I THINK few who have had the good fortune to know Mrs. Patrick Campbell (affectionately known to her contemporaries as " Mrs. Pat ") will quarrel with me when I say that in the world of the theatre, this fascinating woman, as a wit and brilliant conversationalist, had only one rival, Maud Tree. Alone or hunting in couples, woe betide any male or female who felt they could cross swords in verbal encounter with these delicious ladies.

Of Mrs. Pat I am thinking now. I cannot say I have the honour of knowing her well, but being of her time, she came, I saw and *she* conquered. With the figure of a sylph, and a face of beautiful pallor that Rossetti would have raved over, she flashed suddenly on an expectant London in a drama at the Adelphi Theatre entitled " The Trumpet Call." A great emotional star had risen, very nearly the equal of her French and Italian sisters in art, Bernhardt and Duse.

The play she appeared in was of the classic Adelphi type, with a cast which included a bold bad villain, an immaculate hero, a chesnutian funny man, and a suffering heroine.

But while the rest of the persons of the play pursued the usual stereotyped methods known to melodrama, the new-comer, in Mrs. Pat, lifted the threadbare declamatory speeches of Sims and Pettitt (in saying this please do not imagine I am belittling these two famous melodramatic writers, for they were masters of their job and gave the pit and gallery exactly what they wanted and deserved). She

129

lifted all that was usual from a plane which was only designed to obtain sentimental applause into a realm that opened a new book from whose pages a great actress was soon to read tragedy grim in its directness, and pathos—tear-compelling to the last degree. Even the critics sat up and took notice that night, and when one remembers that among this battalion of the first night " death watch " were numbered such men as Clement Scott, Archer, Joseph Knight, and many others who analysed in those days the actors' art through anything but rose-tinted spectacles, the public were made aware " that *some one* had come to town."

As proof of a newcomer's triumph, does not the following incident on that memorable night speak for itself? What, you may ask, was that? Just this. In the third act of " The Trumpet Call," while delivering a speech of great melodramatic power, the waistband of her skirt gave way, and releasing that very (in those days) necessary garment, it slipped to the floor and left our heroine standing in a pair of, I suppose I had better write " bloomers." This appalling catastrophe would, to the ordinary actress, have spelt absolute and total defeat, but such was the way Mrs. Campbell held the house in the palm of her hand, not even a titter was heard, and she carried the situation to its height and its conclusion to a tumult of applause seldom heard in a London theatre.

Mrs. Pat was made. Later, when her brothers and sisters of the theatre became conscious of the exceptional brain possessed by their comrade, it was freely whispered that this—happening—was a well-designed accident. This, however, one can hardly conceive to have been the case, for to run so great a risk would have needed the courage of a lion and the confidence of a Napoleon at the gates of a beleaguered city. I wonder if she will ever tell the truth about this incident. She may, and if it should prove that those who wondered were right, then will I buy all the roses of Picardy and cast them at her feet. It must be difficult to-day for a public who see " The Second Mrs. Tanqueray " revived to realise that on its original production the metropolis gasped at the daring theme of Pinero's masterpiece. A lady of many lovers wedded to the county? Oh! And yet this was so. However was it passed by the censor —everybody inquired? Should the blushing young miss be allowed to witness such a slice of Life? And was it not only the supreme portrayal of a demi-mondaine by a great actress, which gave the elderly an excuse for packing the St. James's Theatre for months and months and months?

It was this Mrs. Tanqueray of the great dark eyes and petulant diction who, taking Mrs. Campbell by the hand, led her from triumph to triumph, even in age to the House of the Matriarch.

In private life there has never been anyone more devastatingly attractive to man and woman alike than Mrs. Pat, and the amusing things she said and says would fill a book.

On one occasion a co-star and herself were not on speaking terms, and the gentleman, rightly or wrongly, getting into his head that his leading lady thought little of his histrionic abilities, sent her a message saying he would be much obliged if Mrs. Campbell would not laugh at him on the stage. To which Mrs. Campbell sent back this answer : " Please give Mr. Jones my kindest regards, and say I never laugh at him on the stage, I always wait until I get home."

In 1929 she sailed for America. Her parting shot as she left this country was : " The London stage only wants flappers and I do not flap."

Her appearance as Eliza Doolittle in Mr. Bernard Shaw's "Pygmalion," I believe, was partly the outcome of her long friendship with the author. It was a remarkable performance, and, of course, it will be remembered that a naughty word made its bow to the public in this play.

It was during the rehearsals of "Pygmalion" that this remarkable lady made a never-to-be-forgotten jest. On inquiring of Mr. Bernard Shaw if it was true that he was a vegetarian, and receiving the answer in the affirmative, she looked at that mighty author quizzically and murmured, "Then, dear Shaw, if you are really a vegetarian, God help the women of England if you ever eat a chop."

Like many a great artist, Mrs. Campbell has ever been over-generous and cared little for money. A mistake no doubt from the point of view of those who live for nothing else. But it was ever thus, for was it not the mightiest of actors, Henry Irving, who, when ill and harassed by financial worries, said plaintively to a friend, "I have lived keeping an army, and I shall die a pauper."

I do not think it is recorded that anybody ever scored off Mrs. Patrick Campbell in a pleasant battle of words, but on one occasion, I believe an actor at rehearsal did reply to her in such a way that, as they say about defeated tennis players, she was left standing.

This member of her company was a good but rather dull performer, and in explaining to him how she wanted a scene played, she said : "You will deliver this very long speech to me with your back to the audience, and I shall be in the centre of the stage listening to you intently, and everything you say I will register on my face."

The actor, naturally disappointed that all the audience would see of him was his neck, replied, "Oh, very well,

Mrs. Campbell, if you say so, but haven't I got a face ? "

To-day Mrs. Pat is in Hollywood amassing, I hope, a fortune, for no one deserves it more than she, bringing joy as she has done into the drab lives of many an ordinary mortal.

I wonder what she thinks of that wonderful city of make-believe. What a book of immense fun she could write about it all, but not of course until she can sit back in well-earned security. This may, we hope, be very soon, for it would be truly illuminating to know what must pass through the mind of a genius who has lived in the atmosphere of Wilde and Shaw, Irving and Terry, Bernhardt and Duse, Guitry and Robertson, a Sargent and a Shannon, a Tree and a Barrie, to find herself being directed by those, many of whom discover the obvious through horn-rimmed spectacles every morning, and sleeping dream of it again.

Still, her great sense of humour may be a lamp that shines happily, enabling her to see " sermons in stones, books in the running scenarios, and good in everything."

I hope devoutly this may be the case.

Oh ! for a film with Mrs. Campbell in a great comedy part, instead of only the magical glimpses we are permitted to catch of her among many who are not fit to polish her lovely histrionic boots.

This may perhaps happen, and when it does how the British public will rise and be grateful.

Alf felt that to dismiss Mrs. Patrick Campbell with a niggardly twelve hundred words was ridiculous, but on looking at the number of names to come, he realised that to do every divinity mentioned justice would have meant the compiling of a biographical encyclopædia.

One thing Alf found Semorix had forgotten, was the description of Mrs. Pat by an American critic, who on hearing of many an acid jest made by her at the expense of those who were sympathetically inclined, during the days when the financial sun had not been shining very brilliantly, he said, " One cannot help admiring this lady's courage ; she is like a sinking frigate firing all her guns at those who would come to her assistance."

The only mistake he made was that Mrs. Campbell was unsinkable.

# MARIE TEMPEST

She is known to her comrades as Maria. I wonder if she realises this, or will it come as a great surprise to her, as it did to Mrs. Kendal when she discovered, by reading an article I wrote about her, that behind her back she was called " Ma K."

Marie Tempest—what does that name spell? Comedy of the highest degree, infinite daintiness, matchless technique, and a shrewd outlook on the art of the theatre, devastating in its accuracy as to what is good, bad and indifferent.

To praise her would be an impertinence, but to say that she has not only gilded lilies, but has painted dandelions and made them take prizes, is a thing at which she, I hope, will not toss her dainty head contemptuously.

In 1887 I worshipped her in " Dorothy."

Five and thirty years ago I had the privilege of being presented to her at Daly's Theatre. Florence St. John, the Queen of Light Opera, was no more, and Marie, stepping into her shoes, put Daly's Theatre on the map, for that manager of managers, the late George Edwardes. I have heard it said, not unkindly, that she is a martinet in the theatre.

Well, of course she must be or she would not be the truly great artist she is. Ever giving of her best, she expects those who support her to do likewise. That she is jealous of her profession and exacting in the playhouse, makes me take off not only my hat, my gloves, and my shoes to her in admiration, but indeed every garment I wear that the Censor would permit me to doff.

From her earliest days in the "Red Hussar," London knelt at her feet, and I well remember George Edwardes taking me into his box on the first night of the "Artist's Model," a great Daly's success, and saying, "Now watch the audience when Marie comes on." For dear Letty Lind, who was her dancing co-star, he told me you will hear the audience on her first appearance say, "Oh!" with affectionate welcome. For Marie you will hear them "Ah!" as they applaud. "They are no less fond of her," he continued, "than they are of Letty, but it will be a reception given to exceptional brilliance, which recognises in a different way extraordinary talent," and his prophecy turned out to be correct. That night this astute man taught me the difference in art between the ephemeral "Oh!" and the lasting "Ah!"

It is curious how, in the theatre, something perhaps which at first appears unimportant in itself, may turn failure into success, and this was so in the case of the comic opera, "Dorothy," which, playing only to £40 a night at the Gaiety Theatre, suddenly jumped into a success of successes, owing to the late Hayden Coffin being given a song called "Queen of My Heart" as an interpolated number when the piece was transferred to another house. I remember this same thing in a lesser degree happening at Daly's in "The Geisha," for although the piece was an outstanding Daly's Theatre hit, running as it did for nearly two years, one of its most successful numbers was an interpolation into Sydney Jones's brilliant score of the "Song of the Goldfish," chosen and made famous by Marie Tempest.

Before the production of this famous light opera there was a gentleman named Phipps, who was engaged to thump the piano at rehearsals. He had never composed anything before, but having written this song, he asked Miss Tempest to hear it, and the rest is history. It is a curious thing to think that this good man never wrote any other particular success; his was indeed a one-song musical life. It may be, of course, that if a Tempest had not sung it so exquisitely, it might have fallen into the limbo of forgotten things, but the fact remains, it did succeed, and its success meant much to the star and the management.

Shrewd to a degree in everything concerning her profession, Marie (may I call her?) has a penetrating wit, and one of the best things she ever said was concerning a long since departed manager, by name Vedrenne, who was celebrated for his honesty and made a point in opening a conversation, in negotiating a contract, of saying, " Now look here, Mr. or Miss So-and-so, I am going to put my cards on the table."

It happened that one evening in a densely crowded restaurant, where our Marie was seated with a friend, that Vedrenne entered and, surveying the room, looked about somewhat bewildered, thinking no doubt that there was nowhere for him to sit and that he would have to dine elsewhere. " Oh ! " said the great actress's companion, " look at Vedrenne. What on earth is he doing standing staring about like that ? " " Oh ! he's all right," said Miss Tempest, " he is only looking for a table to put his cards on."

Worthy of H. J. Byron, and a jest I hope that will never be forgotten.

Like all really grand women, she has never mixed herself in other people's affairs, and one evening, when she was present at a party in which scandal seemed to be the chief topic of conversation, a thing which wearied her considerably, she was divine. One of the Mrs. Candours present, after tearing to shreds the reputation of a much discussed lady, finished her harangue by saying, " Well, as I always say, ' People who live in glass houses should never throw stones,' don't you think so, Miss Tempest ? " " On the contrary," smiled Miss Tempest, " I always think that people who live in glass houses should undress in the dark."

May we hope the laugh that this brought forth caused the vitriolic person to retire, however ungracefully, and cease casting her ill-bred upon the troubled waters.

An anecdote that is always coupled with her at her brightest is about an aspiring actress desiring publicity, of whom she said : " Why put the *and* where the *art* can never be ? " But if it is not authentic, one that is akin is told of the late Sir James Barrie, who, in advising Charles Frohman as to the best way of dealing with an actor who insisted on being featured on the programmes, said, " What I should do is this, my dear Frohman, I should put ' and ' before the name of your leading lady and just ' but ' above the name of this troublesome gentleman."

It was with a certain amount of eagerness that Alf noticed the name of Mrs. Kendal, for although he had never seen her act, he seemed to know her well, so often had he listened to his friend hold forth about this giant among giants.

# MADGE KENDAL

THE greatest all-round actress I ever saw, or I suppose shall ever see, being a genius, was abnormal in her behaviour and, in fact, I may say, not disrespectfully, but rather as an excuse for her, at times a little mad.   Through the courtesy of the *Daily Mail* I am permitted to insert here the small article I wrote at the time of her death, the concluding lines of which I felt at the time, in fairness to her, should be set down.

*September 16th, 1935.*
" MY MRS. KENDAL "—A TRIBUTE.

" I received a command.  I hastened to obey it.

" She was dying and she wished to see me.

" My life has not been without tragic happenings, but my farewell to this mighty actress will remain for ever a dreadful and heart-breaking memory.

" In the drawing-room of a cottage hidden away in the lovely dell of Chorley Wood, I waited and waited for the coming of the tragic figure I was to see for the last time on earth.

" For one long, racking hour I waited.  The strange and mysterious sounds to be heard within a house where Death is clamouring for admittance were everywhere. Never did a door open so slowly as the one I had watched so long and anxiously.

" Supported on either side, hardly able to gain the seat

in the window, through which the sun of a late summer afternoon was streaming, brave beyond words, and undefeated even in her last hour of suffering, My Mrs. Kendal came.

" Her courage and her will were both beyond belief, for not only had she risen from bed, but she had insisted on being dressed with the most scrupulous care.

" In white silk dress, with pale blue surcoat under a flowing over-garment, with diamond buckle at her throat, kid-gloved and elegant, this drooping figure spelt defiance *in excelsis.*

" Left alone, she looked strangely through me and said, ' This is the last time we shall ever see each other.'

" I had no answer.

" It was Mrs. Kendal speaking. I should have insulted her had I then attempted to reply. An hour later I left her. Her head was buried in her arms. She sobbed, and only for a brief moment looked up to say, ' Thank you for coming.'

" The many things she had said between her greeting and farewell were intimate and sacred and will be by me for ever held so. That her last hours of loneliness were full of sorrow and regret for many an opportunity of forgiveness, gone beyond hope of capture, is not to be denied.

" Much she would have wished altered, even at this eleventh hour; indeed, I know. For in half-delirium as she was at times, she asked for comfort she would never have sought in her more guarded hours."

" This may seem strange to mention, I do so because I loved her, and I would ask those who may look upon the memory of her with a less kindly eye (it is not for me to say perhaps without reason) to remember that she was not to be judged by ordinary standards. She was a genius, and as such paid the penalty; the penalty that strife brings in its train, that streak of madness with which abnormal brains are bounded.

"It was thus with her. Let blame, if blame there be, point its finger at the gift and not the frailty.

"For well nigh half a century have I worked with many, and watched well, all the greatest exponents of a long, long day: and as I close my eyes and journey in thought along the coast line of a beautiful and difficult art, the beacon light that shines for me, casting its shadow across the path of many a twinkling star, is the lamp my master held high above her glorious head, supreme in comedy, supreme in tragedy. From her I learned all I know of my profession."

A woman of curious fads, one of the biggest bees that buzzed in Mrs. Kendal's bonnet (a form of head-dress, by the way, which she always affected) was the word "Morality." She herself, being a paragon of Virtue and Matron of the Drama, knew no such word as forgiveness for those who had loved a little too generously. Never did she cease to air her views upon the subject; attacking, horse, foot and artillery, all those who had forgotten to wear a golden circlet on their left hand when electing to take journeys which were brief and ended somewhat suddenly.

No one ever dared argue with her on the point, or attempt to defend the wrong, and it was only when in New York, at a dinner given her by a large gathering of Society women, that she was, I fear, made to look extremely foolish. In her speech at the end of a very interesting function, she devoted a great deal of time to holding forth on her favourite subject, Virtue.

In concluding her address to a somewhat sophisticated and rather astonished audience, she said, "Ladies, this beautiful diamond brooch was given me by the *women of England* for being a Good Woman." When the well-mannered applause had subsided, a witty American lady of irreproachable character rose and said, holding up an equally lovely diamond ornament, "This, ladies, was given to me by the *men of America* for quite the other thing!" What happened when the roars of laughter had subsided, history does not relate.

On her extraordinary gifts as an actress it is unnecessary to dwell, for those who saw her need no telling, while those who had not the good fortune to do so are not, I take it, seeking as an amusement Dramatic Analysis.

One of a very large family, she was, as she said herself, not only born in a theatre but "suckled on grease-paint"; and, indeed, from the crown of her head to the soles of her feet, she was always "a pro." in the very best sense of the word.

At the age of sixteen she played Lady Macbeth to the Macbeth of the man whom Henry Irving took as his model, Samuel Phelps, and was as mighty as a pathetic actress as she was unsurpassed as a comedienne.

She had beautiful chestnut-coloured hair, but there was little else that was extraordinarily striking about her face, except the great intelligence that shone through two small but piercing brown eyes. It was a face, however, that was a sensitive plate on which every emotion she felt was painted clearly and unmistakably.

It was desperately sad to think that this real genius, while being quite untemperamental off the stage, was always deliberately combative, ready to take umbrage at the smallest thing and possessed of a restless spirit which imagined enemies in every thicket. She hated Dramatic Critics and looked upon them either as charlatans or people easy of purchase, and often she went out of her way to be extremely rude to interviewers inquiring—of some inoffensive reporter —what right had he to presume that he knew anything about acting? She secretly admired Henry Irving, but was jealous of the recognition bestowed on him by the Sovereign and bitterly resented the fact that nothing was ever done for her husband.

One of the last things she ever said to me was, " Thank God, Willie was never knighted." This I knew to be bitterness—even in her last hours—at his having been passed over, nor was the fact that she had been made a Dame any consolation.

She herself deserved every honour that there could have been bestowed, and no doubt recognition should have come to her through the man she had married and with whom she had led a most exemplary life. It was all very distressing to see a mighty mind bothering about things which, compared with her contribution to the art of the theatre, and her position with the public, did not amount to a row of pins.

In private life, if ever she had anything devastating to say about her fellows, she had a peculiar habit of emphasising her dislike by giving forth a short snort—a snort into which she was able to put much meaning by lessening or increasing its intensity; and when in high good humour, she invariably added the word " pot " to any adjective or noun. Therefore, people became " duckpots " or " dearpots " or " asspots " or " idiotpots," etc.

Her moods were eight April days rolled into one, and, as a boy, if I saw she was in a somewhat dangerous one at rehearsal, I kept well out of her way. On one occasion, when I could see that any prolonged conversation would lead to a dissertation about something or somebody, I thought I would be extremely discreet and slide by unnoticed if I merely took off my hat and wished her " Good morning." But no ! She was peculiarly restless on this particular day and, instead of saying, " Good morning, Hicks " (she called me " Hicks " all her life), she said, " Yes, Hicks, it *is a* good morning, and I don't think that some of you actors thank God enough for the *good mornings* He gives you." She then proceeded to enlarge on the subject. " Gratitude, Hicks, is the thing seldom found in this profession ; actors are people who "—etc., etc.—so, before I knew it, I was listening to an essay on the frailty of mankind and a dozen other things, through having simply said " Good morning."

Yet, with all her moods, I adored her, for she taught me all I know of a difficult profession, and I always watched her with wide-eyed admiration at rehearsal, for she was a consummate master of everything connected with the theatre.

One curious trait she had, and this was that she never by any chance had any money with her when she went out, and was obliged to borrow even a penny to purchase a newspaper if she wanted one.

To try and manage her if she got an idea into her head was quite impossible, and Kendal, who was a shrewd business man, always knew it was best to let her have her own way and so save more trouble.

While playing " The Ironmaster " at Washington one night, some people in a box were talking during the second act. Directly the curtain fell, she was so enraged that she took me by the hand and, pulling me out of the prompt corner into full view of the audience, pointed at the offenders, saying, "Hicks, look at them; just have a good look at those vulgar wretches, who haven't the remotest notion how ladies and gentlemen ought to behave, etc., etc." Needless to say, I stood aghast. I was only about twenty and didn't even dare to ask her to let me disappear. The papers were full of the incident the next morning.

On the death of Mr. Kendal I received a telegram from her which read, "I am a widow now. Madge Kendal." That was all. And, for some unknown reason, she sent various souvenirs of Kendal to all sorts of people who did not know him particularly well.

G. P. Huntley, a marvellous comic actor if ever there was one, received an old brocaded doublet which her husband had worn many years before as Benedict. Huntley, very surprised and slightly intoxicated at the time the parcel arrived, wired her saying, "Dear lady, many thanks for the cloak. I have found the moths, but you have forgotten to send their eggs."

I hope it will not be felt that, in drawing attention to the eccentricities of a really great person, I am belittling her, for no one ever had a greater admiration for her than I had. These little personal peculiarities that I have written about her, have never, I fancy, appeared in print before, and it is surely the penalty of greatness that trivial things should find a place amidst the unqualified praise bestowed on, and deserved by one of the figures of the Victorian era.

As the teller of a humorous story she had few equals, and her repartee was rapier-like. To Frederick Kerr I heard her say a most amusing thing. Fred Kerr, a delightful exponent of eccentric old men, one evening, being some-what shaky in his lines, apologised to her for a slight lapse or two. " You see, Mrs. Kendal," said Kerr, " I'm sorry I'm a little indistinct, but the fact is I have had a new set of teeth put in to-day." " Oh, have you ! " said the great actress. " Well, I wish you'd put in the old set ; they know the part so much better ! "

The most pathetic words I have ever heard from any human being were those she whispered to me a few hours before her death. They were, " Oh ! what shall I say to God for not having forgiven my children ? " Alas ! alas ! she had quarrelled with them all and had refused to see any of them for many years.


Alf had known Jersey, but never its Lily, although many a tale had he heard of this beautiful lady, who had not only put an island on the map, but had given her name to a face powder manufactured by that celebrated Perruquier, the late William Clarkson, to whom Scotland paid a special tribute by calling an entire county after him. This, of course, being " Wigtown."

# MRS. LANGTRY

JERSEY was full of lovely women when I was in long clothes, and among them, most beautiful of all, was the then Lily le Breton, who afterwards was to take London by storm as the famous Mrs. Langtry.

The Le Breton family are of ancient lineage, and date back in an unbroken line to the eleventh century. Mrs. Langtry's mother, whom I remember well as an old lady, must have been beautiful in her youth. Her father, the Dean of Jersey, was a singularly handsome man, and, looking a Dean to the life, was gifted with an extraordinary photographic memory. It is said that he was able to read through a column of *The Times* only once and then recite it immediately afterwards with hardly a mistake.

Well was the daughter of these two charming and picturesque people named " The Jersey Lily," for she was more to be likened to that stately flower than any other, hers being a cold beauty and her grey eyes having but little warmth in them. Beneath, however, an exterior which attracted every male in the community upon whom she smiled, and at the same time made them all stand slightly in awe of her, there was a heart of gold and a sense of humour which was divine.

I suppose as much rubbish has been written about Mrs. Langtry as of any well-known beauty who ever lived. Everything she did was magnified a thousandfold, and when rumour ran dry, idle tongues concocted absurdities about her, even to the spreading of quite untrue reports, one of these being that one night she had flopped an ice down the neck of a royal personage.

How little the idiots who invented such nonsense understood Lily Langtry! If they had only known her even slightly they would have realised that as a great lady she was born, as a great lady she lived, and as a great lady she died. But table talk and scandal were welcome guests in the eighties, and Lily le Breton as a girl was of that day, a day when the hypocrisy connected with the vapours and the crinoline was only just disappearing. It had given place to the smug, presumed respectability of the 'eighties, a time when even engaged couples were only permitted to murmur their sweet nothings to each other in the presence of third parties. Those were the days when the women of the stage were looked upon as a whole with pious horror, and imagined by the parochial mind to be little better than street-walkers. Small wonder, then, that when Mrs. Langtry, with the eyes of the world upon her, the object of royal admiration, petted by Society and painted by Millais, elected to become an actress, her every step was watched by the jealous in the hope that she would be caught tripping.

Success came to her from all sides. She was successful in the theatrical profession, successful on the turf, and successful in securing the love of countless friends. She was never a great actress, and I'm sure she never pretended to be one. But she brought to all her work grace of manner, great distinction, and a high intelligence, and walked the stage as few women have ever walked it. She moved like a beautiful panther.

It was while playing in a piece called " Peril "—in which she had, I think, her greatest success—that she made a slip of the tongue one night, which, as she told me, not only made the audience rock with laughter, but ruined the second act of the play. At the end of a love scene she had to say, "Very well then, but there are people coming ; let us seek a cosy nook " ; by mistake she whispered, " Let us seek a nosey cook. . . ."

When this Victorian effort was revived at the Garrick Theatre many years ago, it did not succeed as it had succeeded before, and on someone saying, " I see that ' Peril ' is coming off at the Garrick," that brilliant talker, the late Comyns Carr, said, " I shall have to ask them next Sunday to be sure to sing that beautiful hymn, ' For those in Peril at the G.' "

In private life she was the most natural woman possible and took the greatest pleasure in simple fun and amusement.

Many a summer's afternoon have my wife and myself spent shrimping and bathing with her in her beloved little island, picnicking on the rocks, all of us happy as any three London trippers who ever visited Margate from a Saturday till Monday.

A wonderful woman of the world was " The Jersey Lily," possessed of infinite charm and great tact.

She sleeps in the little cemetery which surrounds the church of St. Saviour, where she worshipped as a child and where her father officiated for so many years.

Visiting the island of my birth some few months ago, I made a pilgrimage to place some flowers on the grave of my lifelong friend, and I was amazed to see a large marble bust of her, which, without wishing to belittle the talents of the sculptor, whose name I do not know, was as much like Mrs. Langtry as I am like David Garrick. I suppose it does not matter much what succeeding generations think of the appearance of any public favourite, but I do hope that some day this strange effort will be removed, or, in years to come, those who visit St. Saviour's cemetery will imagine that our ideas of a beautiful woman must have been quaint indeed.

Nor far from where she lies rests a comrade of hers and a dear friend of mine, that grand actor, Henry Kemble (a nephew of Fanny Kemble). He sleeps beneath a plain earthen mound with no headstone to mark his last earthly habitation. That this should be so was his last request. He was a strange and eccentric old gentleman in many ways and, though loved by a host of friends in London, elected to journey to Jersey when he knew his fatal illness was upon him, there to die along among strangers.

Innumerable stories were connected with the name of dear Henry Kemble, who would, were he alive to-day, be the first not to mind my saying that sometimes he wore Ibsen's vine leaves in his hair. It was at a dress rehearsal at the Comedy Theatre that, having dined unwisely and too well, he looked at a huge safe in a scene which was laid in a city office, and turning to Charles Hawtrey said, " Dear, dear, dear, look at that dreadful safe. Why have a wooden one painted, when an iron one would have done just as well ? " He was possessed of a sharp tongue on occasions, and to a youthful Guardsman, who was quite unaware that the old gentleman sitting opposite him was most dangerous in the small hours, and who thought he could cross swords with him with impunity, he said, " Young gentleman, I cannot think where I have met you before," and, after a moment's pause, continued, " Oh, yes ! I do remember ! Once at a public house in Oldham." The remark was quite ridiculous and the more so as I do not suppose the youthful soldier had ever heard of Oldham. There was a laugh at the boy's expense, and Kemble, rising majestically from the table, bade the fellow members of his club good night, turning at the door as he did so, and looking at his friend from Oldham said, " Meet me to-morrow at the Marble Arch. I shall not be there."

# LADY BANCROFT

WHO, before her distinguished husband received the honour of knighthood, was the idol of London as Marie Wilton, is of course quite unknown to present-day playgoers, and the percentage of people who saw this inimitable comedienne in the hey-day of her success must be infinitesimal, for she had retired many a long year before her lamented death in 1926.

I had the good fortune to see her play in the first revival of " Diplomacy " at the Garrick Theatre, when that most distinguished actress, Olga Nethersole, appeared as the Countess Zicka, and sweet Kate Rorke was the Dora of Sardou's (as far as the English theatre is concerned) master-piece. Oh! what a delicious figure of fun was this Queen of Comedy, and how the house laughed at her lengthy description of the Berne Clock, a speech by the way, which was interpolated especially for her into the play on its original production at the Haymarket Theatre in the early 'eighties, when a cast which included the never-to-be-surpassed Forbes Robertson, so recently passed away, a giant among giants, Squire Bancroft, reposeful and deliberate, and Arthur Cecil, not so much an actor as a society droll, were members of the wonderful company the Bancroft management had gathered about them.

I knew Lady Bancroft very well as an old lady, and her sense of fun and her charm and attraction were with her even when she had passed her allotted span.

In her age, as she sat, hostess at her house in Berkeley

Square, she appeared, what the bright young things would describe to-day, as " a perfect Pet." Lady Bancroft was a round, fat, little figure, with a divinely attractive face in which were set two tiny eyes, twinkling with merriment and missing nothing that came within their orbit.

Throughout her life she was a martyr to that distressing malady, hay-fever, and as the merry month of May came round each season so surely did her twinkling eyes stream in torrents, even if they were miles away from the pollen-laden country-side, beloved by bees and other short-tempered insects.

Mentioning the Bees, reminds me that Sir Squire Bancroft and his lady were known to their friends as such. As Theatre Partners they were the first to introduce natural acting, not the ineffective natural mumbling which to-day is at times very much in evidence, but apparent naturalness, which is art, and quite another thing. They were also the first to do away with painted canvas doors and substituted wooden lintels, an enormous innovation in the middle 'seventies ; while beautiful furniture, cut glass, real pictures, priceless ornaments and the silver salver, were seen by the astonished public at the little Prince of Wales Theatre off the Tottenham Court Road, when the Bancrofts introduced the Robertson comedies to delighted Metropolitan audiences.

Lady Bancroft's partner, " B " of the ebony-rimmed eyeglass and wavy silver hair, six feet of distinguished and handsome manhood, was one of the best business men ever connected with the theatre, as he died leaving a fortune of some hundred and eighty thousand pounds, and though a large proportion of this was, of course, made in the play-house, judicious speculation had much to do with the amassing of this enormous sum.

He was beyond words, to all he came in contact with,

kindly, helpful and delightful, a modern Touchstone, though much more amusing than that boring Shakespearean clown. He made it a boast that he always set aside £50 a year for wreaths and wedding presents. He attended the funerals of all his distinguished friends.

Shrewd, too, was he in his choice of words in giving advice, and extremely careful never to commit himself to any definite critical opinion, generally dodging the issue with a well-turned phrase.

Only a few years ago he left us at the age of eighty-four, still young in figure and alert of mind.

While my profession owes an undying debt of gratitude to Henry Irving for lifting it out of the rogue and vagabond period, it must never be forgotten by my comrades how much the yare also indebted for the dignity brought to their calling by dear Squire and the marvellous lady née Wilton, afterward Lady Bancroft.

It was tantalizing to Alf to find after reading about Lady Bancroft that he again had stumbled upon another celebrity who had forsaken the stage while he was still at school. If Semorix were right, a wave of regret was his that he seemed to be living, by comparison with the 'eighties, in an early Woolworth Renaissance.

"Still," he muttered, "in years to come perhaps I shall make the mouths of the unborn water when they read what I shall write about those who are my contemporaries."

After delving lovingly into a well-deserved tribute to Ellaline Terriss, for he was among the thousands who are devoted to her, all he said to himself was:

"I couldn't have done better myself, though it's not half good enough."

## ELLALINE TERRISS

To write in glowing terms of a lady one dislikes intensely is difficult enough, but to be set the task of writing about a woman one adores, is to be asked to engage in an almost Herculean effort.

My first impulse is to search the dictionary for added superlatives, but if I did this, my readers would very probably take the advice of the first grave-digger and get them to yawn.

Therefore, in speaking of my Ella, who has put up with me for four and forty years, I will content myself by saying that I owe everything in the world to her, that my gratitude is eternal, and that my life, if it were asked of me, for her would be gladly given.

Her real name is Mary Lewin, a pretty, almost Barrieish name, I have always thought, and as the daughter of that famous actor, William Terriss, began her stage career in the great school of Charles Wyndham, who took a pride in calling her his Dramatic God-child.

Ella never set out to be or pretended that she was a great actress, for the word greatness in theatre-land is, as a rule, reserved for those who play tragedy or are recognised as exponents of classic comedy in its highest flights.

But thinking quite dispassionately of this lovely creature, I have not the slightest compunction in saying that in her own especial line she was beyond words magnificent. Few of her contemporaries could hold a candle to her in the singing of the songs she made famous, and she brought to everything she did a charm, a gaiety and a distinction, of the kind possessed by Auntie Nell, otherwise Ellen Terry, who loved her and whom she loved so dearly.

At the age of twenty-two Ellaline forsook Pinero comedies and became the first of a long line of famous " Girls " who had for a father the immortal George Edwardes. As the " Shop Girl," " My Girl," " The Runaway Girl " and " The Circus Girl," she infused into the old Gaiety Theatre an entirely new atmosphere. Its audiences previously accustomed to the genius of Nellie Farren, welcomed the newcomer with open arms, and she bound them to her heart with " A little bit of string."

As a divine wife she receives my tribute, as a great little artist she needs from me no platitudinous approbation. In these thumbnail sketches of grand ladies of the stage I have endeavoured not so much to import criticism of work done as to mention intimate things, which were either curious or might delight those who, not knowing their favourites personally, had been obliged to love them from across that mighty barrier, a row of footlights. So let me leave the working side of my brilliant partner's life and think at random of the many simple things that made for happiness, not only for her in her leisure hours, but also for those who are counted her friends. These are indeed legion.

As a fisherman she has killed many a good fish in the tumbling waters of the Spey and brought skilfully to bank those tigers of our southern streams, the flashing rainbow and the gaily spotted trout.

Our comradeship in sport has been one of our greatest joys, and to watch her bring down a right and left from a butt or over dogs on a Scottish moor, has many a time made up for the gale-assisted blackcock I have myself succeeded in missing.

Never have I heard her blame anybody or say an unkind thing even about those whose actions she might well have been entitled to resent.

During the last five and forty years she has only had four ladies' maids (all of whom left to get married). This surely is proof, if one were needed, that she is a gentle and kindly mistress. For thirty years we acted continuously together, and during that time I had the privilege of writing many of her greatest successes, which included her parts in such plays as " The Runaway Girl," " Bluebell in Fairyland," " The Catch of the Season," " The Cherry Girl," " Sleeping Partners," " The Man in Dress Clothes," and many another.

She never made heavy weather of the work, however hard, her great sense of fun standing her in good stead. I remember how she laughed when rehearsing a children's song called " The Sunflower and the Sun."

She noticed that there were only eleven sunflower little children and there ought to have been twelve, and on inquiring why this was, she was told by a little urchin that the reason they were one short was that the twelfth sunflower was being sick under the stage.

Many were the practical jokes she played on me in the theatre, but never was I taken in so completely as at an audition one afternoon. Dozens of girls had had their voices tried, when an old lady appeared on the stage, and after singing a verse of " Kathleen Mavourneen," collapsed and had to be carried off to the wings. I was thoroughly upset, and I told the stage manager not to be such an owl as to allow old people like that to ask for chorus work.

About an hour afterwards, Ella joined me in the stalls

and asked me if I had discovered any rising talent. I said, "Not up to now," but that I had had a most painful experience, and explained to her that they had allowed a poor old lady to try to sing and that she was so nervous that she fainted and had to be put into a cab I had ordered. She let me go on saying it was cruel to encourage half-witted old people, etc., etc., and when I had finished looked up slyly and said, "It was very kind of you to order a cab for me, but it wasn't a very good one, so I sent it away."

Ella had gone to endless trouble to dress up and with the whole company in the joke, had succeeded in getting a real good laugh at my expense.

At the first rehearsal of "Alice in Wonderland" at the Vaudeville, in which she played Alice for some three hundred performances, she put on a pinafore and, looking as young as any of the children, asked the chorus master, who did not know her by sight, if she could have a little something to do. This astute gentleman heard her sing one verse of a song and then said, "No, you go home and tell your mother you are not good enough." He was, of course, wrong, but I often wonder how many of us who have made our little names, if we applied unlabelled for work to those who did not know us, would get a job. Probably very few.

In the Gaiety days she was christened by Lionel Monckton, that most charming of composers, "the Rock of Gibraltar," because, although shaking with fear as we all do on first nights, she never appeared to be the slightest bit nervous. It was in "The Runaway Girl" that, being given a lyric at the eleventh hour, she forgot the words entirely, and sang a meaningless jumble of nonsense. At the end of the performance Ivan Caryll, whose English at that time was anything but faultless, came round and said, "Ella, you were wonderful, but I didn't like the words of the new song I wrote for you. We must get a better lyric written."

It was Ellaline Terriss who originated concert-parties for the front in the Great War, and organising a splendid troupe of artists, landed in France on Christmas Eve. In begging permission at the War Office to be allowed to appear in France, I was asked by Lord Kitchener when we proposed to go. "On Christmas Eve, sir," I replied. "Oh, really," said the great soldier rather sarcastically, "are you under the impression we are going to stop fighting on Christmas Day?" To which, being extremely hurt, I rather angrily replied, "I haven't the faintest idea, have you?"

Several gentlemen with red bands round their hats shook in their shoes, expecting me, no doubt, to be sent to the Tower, but Kitchener, feeling probably that he had not made a very kind remark, looked at me and said politely, "You want to go and amuse the troops, I see. Well, that's very thoughtful of you; I will give orders that you get into communication with Sir John French at once."

During our visit to one of the base hospitals, a poor young soldier, who was badly wounded, hearing that Miss Terriss was in the building, begged that he might speak to her. To the dimly-lit corner where the poor fellow lay, Ella went. He could only just whisper, but he said, "Oh! would you be so kind as to sing the 'Honeysuckle and the Bee,' I should like to hear it once again. I've often heard you sing it at the Vaudeville."

So she knelt down by his bed and sang very, very gently. He thanked her with a sigh and closed his eyes with a happy smile upon his face. Poor boy, from what we gathered he was soon to close them for ever.

I may say that to be amusing with a lump in your throat

and struggling to keep back your tears, standing among men, who lie swathed in field dressings, is an experience that would break the nerve of anyone not possessed of a heart of stone.

Ellaline Terriss has now retired, after having been an actress for fifty years, and has left me, as she amusingly puts it, " to try and earn the dog biscuits."

To-day the hair of the loveliest Cinderella of all time is snow-white, but to me she is, and will ever be, more beautiful even than she was in those far-off days, forty-four years ago, when, after an eleven-day courtship, she said " I will " in a little Registrar's Office in Brentford High Street.

Alf almost clapped his hands with joy when he saw the name of everybody's Alice Delysia as the heading of a new chapter.

Critics are not supposed to applaud, but many a time had Alf forgotten himself in the Theatre when he had been paid to sit in judgment on this ray of French Dramatic Sunshine.

# ALICE DELYSIA

A GREATER artist than even the public know—despite the fact that they are never tired of singing her praises from the housetops. For they have never seen her in a great classic role, not necessarily in the draperies of Olympus, but in the happiest flights of Desazet and Réjane. I wait and wait to see her step on the stage—serene and self-possessed, demanding and obtaining homage as Marguerite Gautier, from the world of Bohemia over which that ill-fated and tragic figure reigned.

It is to be hoped, dear Alice, that forgetting you ever sang so charmingly, you one night will creep out and peeping down a corridor, steal from the greatest of Dumas' heroines the shoes she has left for you outside a long closed door.

Never in my life have I come across a more open-handed, open-hearted, generous human being than Delysia. Sophisticated in her work, she is a child off the stage, pleased with simple things, grateful for a trifling kindly act. Sad for those in trouble, glad with those who are happy, and ever ready to praise a rival—and incapable of saying anything that might hurt.

Among her comrades she is given the highest praise as a woman, when they call her a good fellow, and a good trouper; she is both of these.

The word trouper may not be understood by my readers, as it is a word which is connected purely with my profession—but I can explain it this way. A trouper means some one who never grumbles, who works continually and uncomplainingly, is ready to stand by the ship in distress, or the captain—who is heading for the storm; a support to the weak and a help to the strong, and one who might well have inspired Kipling to write " If." This is Delysia.

I think I am right in saying that she made her first appearance in England under Charles B. Cochran's management at the time Harry Fragson appeared under the banner of that great showman in revue. Poor Fragson! a merry fellow, who met a sudden tragic and untimely end. He was shot by his own father, the poor old man having lost his reason, imagining that he had lost the love of a son who was in fact absolutely devoted to him. I can see Fragson now—a superlatively good singer of light songs of the boulevard at the piano, he was one of the greatest masters of compelling an audience to continue their applause I have ever seen. He would rise from the piano, face them, bow and hesitate whether he should leave the stage or not, rub his hands in an apologetic sort of way, and apparently wavering as to what was the right thing to do, conveyed the impression that he wondered if his reception was possible —was it really all true? Do you want to hear me again? No, it can't be! And then he would take his place again at the piano with a humility that was compelling. A remarkable seller of first-class material was Harry Fragson, and a great favourite not only with those who applauded him, but also with all who knew him in private life.

After her association on the London stage with Fragson, Delysia became the rage, under the management of Mr. Cochran, and these successes are so recent that it is unnecessary to speak of them.

A fervent patriot, Delysia's fanatical love for her dear

France was a thing which gave her listeners a tremendous uplift and put heart into those who in the dark hours of the war were weary and would have welcomed an even inconclusive peace. Of such stuff as a patriot was Joan of Arc, but no medieval saint would have gone singing to her death, more supremely happy that she gave her life for the salvation of her country, than Alice Delysia. In 1916 news came that her brother had been wounded. At her house that night she was entertaining many members of the French Embassy and quite a number of French officers, and it was on this occasion I saw a new tragedienne—her name was Delysia. After supper she was asked to sing. She declined to do so, but in refusing said, " If you like I will try to entertain you, but not with song. Let me recite the *Marseillaise*."

Her guests were grateful, but I am sure secretly disappointed. The " Marseillaise " was a threadbare garment to them. I can see the picture now, a crowded salon and Delysia standing up with men in uniform, where many others were seated at her feet.

The chatter ceased. The silence of death fell upon the room, as with almost a shout this woman of Revue fame cried aloud in defiance and agony of mind : " *The Marseillaise* "!!! Her voice was charged with pathos, beneath which one felt enduring hate for the aggressor, and an inspired reverence for those who had fallen at the gates of Verdun.

Delysia, her head thrown back, her hair in a tangle, white-lipped and wide-eyed—was indeed France.

So intense and tremendous was her rendering of lines which those who listened knew by heart, that they became as something they had never understood or heard before. The soul of a patriot had left London and was wandering amidst a throng of blue-coated men searching for a loved one who had stood sentinel. The figure of a woman was in the room, but Delysia herself was otherwhere. It was an exalting spectacle, and tears streamed down the cheeks of the Frenchmen who heard and the Englishman who was her guest was unashamed that his eyes, too, were dimmed. Her brother lived—the guns are silent. May they ever remain so.

To my dear friend as a happy woman I return. May it not be long before I see her smiling face again, and hope that in those great hours of the morning, so inaptly named "the small," I shall watch her, in her kitchen, dealing with eggs and bacon, for added to her many other accomplishments, Alice Delysia, like a host of her charming country-women, is a chef *par excellence*.

It is quite right, thought our book-reviewing friend, that Yvonne should find herself so close to her Parisian sister, Alice, for as H. J. Byron remarked in a famous play, "Alike and yet unlike, they are two roses." It was Charles Wyndham who one night, during the run of this play, altered the line by mistake and said, looking at Mary Moore and Ellaline Terriss, "Alike and yet unlike, they have two noses."

How wisely chosen was her name. Spring! That most
glorious of all the seasons, when Nature showers hope upon
a waiting world, with its buds and its blossoms and its
gentle breezes and its promise of greater things to come.
Printemps—I met her first in 1918. I was at supper with
Lucien and Sacha at their London hotel (her father-in-law
and husband), and as she had come in late, and I was
unexpected, having been introduced to Sacha for the first
time that evening, she hadn't the remotest idea who I was
until Lucien, who had known me all my life, told her he
thought I was an actor, and Sacha said, "He is playing in
my play, 'Sleeping Partners.'" I suppose it dawned suddenly
on her that I was someone she had heard of, for she jumped
up and kissed me and spent the rest of the evening saying
to herself in French that she ought to have known my name.
I kept telling her in my best doggerel that there was no
reason why she should even know that I existed, but she
would have none of it, and I found myself continually under
the fire of a pair of sparkling eyes which she pretended
were asking for forgiveness, as she smiled comically the while.
Later I wrote the following of her and my dear Sacha :

"Sacha and Yvonne—what a marvellous pair they are!
I speak of them off the stage ; the world is quite aware how
incomparable they are on it. They are both unique and
adorable—neither of them quite perfect without the other.

"To be with them is like drawing aside the curtain of

some drowsy common-place room and letting in a flood of sunshine. Their smile opens an obstinate window and on the instant Beauty, Brains, Vitality and Infinite Charm trip across the floor of one's heart and, setting many a forgotten ornament in its place, turn modern mental confusion into order and, consequently, delight.

" It is not because I love them dearly that I am carried away and appear to be extravagant in my appreciation of my two real friends—I have enough intelligence not to allow sentiment to lull criticism into a happy impotence. I have known them many years now, and they are the lovely annuals in the herbaceous border of my life, to whose coming I look forward each Spring—flowers of Art to be watched over tenderly by me throughout the summer and to be thought of during the wintry days their petals are hidden, with the knowledge they will return to me in the months to come, if possible, even more to be admired.

" Their life together is an ideal one. How much they admire each other it would be difficult to conjecture. She —his genius ; he—her beauty allied to a brain which, although borrowing from him much, has always like a faithful creditor returned his loan with extravagant interest. It is true that he has delved for diamonds and, having found them, cut them into many facets, but she has given the gems their setting and the audiences of the world have seen her wearing them with admiration and delight.

" To-day Sacha speaks admirable English, but Yvonne, electing to remain silent in any language but her own, speaks volumes with her eyes, her hands and a personal magnetism which makes one wonder if Nature has not been a little too prodigal in flinging so much of her most precious gifts into the lap of one individual."

Having written thus of these two wonderful artists, there is nothing here that I can or would write of my heartache at their parting. It is history. I think that the wives of men of genius have nearly always been profoundly stupid individuals or they could never have put up with the abnormal brains possessed by husbands who in lucid intervals of insanity proposed marriage to them. When, therefore, in the case of two brilliant Latin temperaments electing to become *one*, the fact may be forgiven that when on Life's Highway they came to a signpost on which was painted the words Right and Left they disagreed as to which road led to Happiness Corner. However, being a purely private affair, it is no concern of ours. All one can say with a sad smile is, " May our profound loss be their gain."

It is strange to remember that the inimitable Alice Delysia and Yvonne Printemps both migrated from the same school, the Châtelet. I think it was there as girls they appeared in practically little more than thinking parts ; of the former I have spoken, of the latter, through all the delightful hours that I have spent in her company, I never knew her to be anything but care-free and delicious. My French is awful, and in 1918, the early days of our friendship, she did not know one word of English. I remember one night while she was at supper with Lucien, Sacha and myself, that in my endeavour to say how fond I was of her in my best Parisian Berlitz, she threw up her hands and, screaming with laughter, did a comic fall off her chair on to the floor. Lucien laughed heartily and wagged his head, and Sacha joined also in the merriment. I couldn't make out what had happened till Sacha said, " You have not told her you love her, Seymour. You have said you would like to be her lover." I apologised profusely and said how sorry I was to have made such a terrible mistake. " Oh! " said my host, " why are you upset? *Wouldn't* you like to be her lover? " Who but a Frenchman could have thought of such an unanswerable question?

Yvonne never seemed to me to care about dressing elaborately off the stage, and more often than not wore tweeds, to which she added a dainty little hat and a silk scarf twisted apparently carelessly round her neck, held together by some beautiful ornament.

Who of those who saw her will ever forget her Mozart, or let memory, that greatest cheat of all, lull into forgetfulness the bird-like notes which fell from a throat that throbbed for the world's pleasure.

But not only as a singer and the daintiest of comediennes was she outstanding, for, in that tragic play " Jacqueline " she was marvellous, making the mighty Lucien, as he said himself, give of his greatest. Ah! what a man was this father of an extraordinary son, his dear Sacha!

At a time he was about to open in London and was asking me what the Princes Theatre was like, of which I was lessee. I replied it was a fine house and could accommodate a big audience. Coming to look at it, he said, " Yes, it is a good house, and the decorations, how would you describe them? " I said, " I don't quite know." He said, " I do. *Décor Napoléon quatre.*" What Noel Coward understands of the stage from every angle, so it is with Sacha Guitry! Even apart from acting they are the two greatest theatre men it has been my lot to fall in with during my fifty years' apprenticeship in their profession. To think that Sacha has invited me in 1938 to play with him in Paris, and film the play afterwards is a compliment which would cure even my inferiority complex, if it were possible. I could not be more honoured. That we were born in different countries makes little difference, for the language we speak—when in each other's company—is the most beautiful in the world. It is the language of the heart.

And now, my incomparable Yvonne, in bidding you *au revoir*, I place this very inadequate tribute at your dainty feet, conscious of the fact that I have a small place in your memory, and that you know you have a very large one in mine as a sweet woman and a divine artist. Till the clock strikes my hour—I am for ever yours, Yvonne.

# LADY TREE

THE British stage has only recently lost a divinely amusing lady, and not only a great actress, but a great scholar, and what is perhaps better than all these things, one of the most devoted mothers and grandmothers that ever lived. Somehow I was always a little frightened of her, for her knowledge of the world was profound, and she had an uncanny quality of being able to turn the most innocent remark into a jest that, which even if you only valued yourself at sixpence, made you appear fourpence to the assembled company.

What dear Herbert Tree owed to her tact and judgment only those who knew him will ever know, and I knew him extremely well. And how brave and courageous was Maud Tree. For years Mistress of the Haymarket and afterwards at Her Majesty's, she was a queen of theatreland, guiding and advising, a hostess of hostesses, a great lady in every sense of the word. After the lamented death of her distinguished partner, she was still the never-complaining, brilliant woman who, working single-handed for other managements, plucked the rose as it bloomed, and faced the wintry winds as they blew.

As a boy I heard such men as Lord Tennyson and Henry Irving, Whistler and a score of giants whom it was my privilege to sit and listen to, declare that Ellen Terry was supreme as Ophelia. (Alas, I was too young to have seen her!) But as a man by far the best Ophelia I ever saw was the Ophelia of Maud Tree. Into the Mad Scene she imported the wistful sadness of her charm. Here was a gentle madness, something born of a great, and to her, intelligible happening. Her Maid of Denmark made one pity Hamlet the more in his loss of her, for she was very real and in watching o'erthrown this sweet and child-like mind, tears came easily. Maud Tree's Ophelia always made me think, Oh! if it were only possible to set back the universe and give her yesterday. In many an ordinary part she never failed, and in her own line of comedy she was unrivalled. Later she trod the path of broader methods, and could by look or word paint a world of meaning into an ordinary picture by comic vagueness or wondering alarm in a farcical situation.

More years ago than I care to remember (I believe this is the correct way of prefacing something that happened some time back, though as everyone should be extremely proud of remembering a happy past, why people apologise for Time I have yet to understand) I was sitting next to Lady Tree at a dinner given by Charles Wyndham, I think, in honour of the then Sir Alfred Mond. There were some twenty guests present and speeches became the order of the evening, those ghastly stringings together of platitudes, which have hopes of becoming epigrams as they nod drowsily to the port and brandy. To my horror, being the youngest person present, I was told I must propose Sir Herbert Tree's health. Not having the slightest idea what to say in the company of distinguished people, I begged Lady Tree to get me excused. "Certainly not," she said, "you have nothing to be nervous about; I'll give you a toast of just one line. As Herbert is playing Julius Cæsar at the moment, all you need do is to raise your glass and, looking sadly at him, say 'Gentlemen, we come to bury Cæsar, not to praise him!'"

Herbert Tree was a man of infinite wit, and one of the best things he ever said was his reply to an inquiry as to what he thought of " Chu Chin Chow," which made such a fortune for all concerned at His Majesty's, that playhouse which he always spoke of as " my beautiful theatre." He had been strongly opposed to the production of this most successful, musical entertainment, and, indeed, had he not been in America an agreement for its production at London's premier house would never have been signed. However, those protecting his financial interests in England, which at the moment were, shall we say, in need of adjustment, arranged with Oscar Ashe to appear at His Majesty's on sharing terms. The result is a matter of theatrical history. On Tree's arrival in London he at once elected to see the performance, and watching a crowding house applauding to the echo its every item, he leaned back moodily in his box, thinking no doubt of Shakespearean productions, and wondering how fate had decreed that Musical Comedy had almost taken its place in his highbrow home. Towards the middle of the evening many a dancing girl with very few clothes to cover her, gyrated voluptuously before his eyes, and it was at this point, when asked what he thought of it all, he said, " Ah, it is charming, but I fear it is more ' navel than millinery,' " a jest for which full marks must certainly be given. This was a witticism absolutely in the Lady Tree vein, and I am sure if it had not been made by the celebrated lessee, himself, she would ultimately have said it with that innocent inquiring stare of hers.

During the enormously successful run of " Chu Chin Chow," Lady Tree made a most amusing remark while seated in a Pullman Car opposite an extremely stout lady who was nursing a Chow and eating buns at the same time. Looking at the double chin of the dog-lover and watching her munching so pleasantly, she said to her companion, "I know what that woman is doing, she is advertising our success." "How do you mean?" asked the lady she addressed. "Well, my dear," said Maud Tree, looking at her friend, "could anything be more obvious, '*Chew ! Chin ! ! Chow ! ! !*'" Space does not permit me to set down the hundreds of witty things that appear on the credit of this dear lady's life book, but one thing which comes to my mind and must not be forgotten, was her quip at a meeting of ladies discussing women's rights in the days before the petticoat imagined it had not got the vote (it has really had it from the days of Cleopatra). In praising men she said, "Husbands are necessities we should all be thankful for, but there is one thing which I should like to advise, and it is this. Always look with an inquiring eye when your lesser half brings you an unexpected present, for it is generally a gesture of contrition for having done something wrong. So much do I believe this that I have always called these unsolicited donations not Alibi, but Ali Buy-Buy presents." Not too bad I think it will be agreed.

I had the honour of knowing and loving her for over forty years, and it was with the deepest grief I stood dumbfounded when I read a placard which told me I should never see her again.

# GERTRUDE LAWRENCE

It has been truly said that it is " only differences of opinion which make horse racing," and therefore I should be as incurable an optimist as was the cat that sat on the dome of St. Paul's waiting for a lark if I supposed for a moment, that, in saying I think Gertrude Lawrence is the finest all-round actress on the British stage to-day, I should not be challenged ! This, of course, may not happen.  Still, if it does, be that challenge either from the professional critic, the jealous or the unknowledgable, I, holding this honest opinion, shall say so still.  " Oh ! " I have heard it said, " yes, she's splendid, but only at her best when she is under Noel Coward's guiding hand."  But supposing this to be true, what of it ?  A curtain rises, a player frets his hour upon the stage.  It is not our province to question how or why we have been moved to laughter, tears and profound admiration.  Is not the pleasure we have derived from seeing something superlatively *good* enough ?  And as with Miss Lawrence I have shed tears, laughed and forgotten the struggle, so to her I have given the unbounded adulation of a loyal subject to his queen.  In the Irish Players we saw such perfection of acting that, as we watched, we lived and suffered with them—forgetting we were at a Theatre.  Sinclair, what an actor—that " darling man " Morgan (to me he can never be dead), and that great artist, Sara Allgood—what a trio in " Juno and the Paycock." Surely a Munden, a Matthews and a Mrs. Pritchard were these.

173

And so did we see in the triple bills of Noel Coward a similar matchless team led by a master and mistress in the art of the theatre. Gertie Lawrence—in these plays—ran the gamut of the emotions—not as a witty American writer wrote of a much heralded actress from A to B, but from one end of the dramatic alphabet to the other. In " Fumed Oak " she was Marie Wilton ; in " Red Peppers " Nellie Farren ; in " Shadow Dance " Jane Hading—only better than the French actress, for Hading neither sang nor danced. So carried away was I with the genius of it all that I had the temerity to send her the shoes worn by Lady Bancroft as Peg Woffington, and one of the few prints in existence of Rachel as Camille ; when I had done so I was fearful that she might think the offering an impertinence on my part, but instead of which I received within an hour one of the most generous and charming letters I have ever had the pleasure of placing in an autograph book, between whose covers lie memories of Garrick and Kean, Mrs. Siddons and Ellen Terry, and a host of other immortals. To my friend of years, Noel, I ventured to give the sword which Henry Irving treasured—the sword that Edmund Kean wore as " Brutus "—and what do you think this enthusiast did ? A telephone bell rang in my dressing-room at the theatre and a voice I knew said : " Is your curtain down ? " I said, " Just." It was Noel Coward speaking. He replied, " So is mine—don't leave, wait for me—I am coming straight down to you." He came, and we didn't leave my room till long after—the playhouse was in darkness and its only occupant the fireman going his solitary round. That evening will live long in my memory, for I spent it not only with a man I am proud to take off my hat to, but a human being who, with the world at his feet, was simple and understanding, and who, in talking of his hopes and fears, might have been a youthful student on the threshold of his career.

I had been going through a difficult time, but when we parted I was happy and elated and quite prepared to rehearse for my next failure (if such the coming play should turn out to be) with courage and a certainty that the theatre could never die. During the night we had spoken much of Lawrence and I asked him if he had to " produce " her very much. " Far from it," my friend replied. " Perhaps I sometimes may suggest that it would be wiser not to do this or that—but nothing more ! " Not, I am sure, that she would have resented being clay in such a potter's hand—for it is only the great artist who knows how little he knows and is learning, learning, learning, even till Twilight Time. My first impression of Gertrude Lawrence, the woman apart from the actress, was one of quite over-whelming femininity. Her large grey eyes sparkled with fun as we talked, and her up-tilted nose had an impudent sense of humour. She will forgive me, I know, if I put her down as devastatingly attractive rather than conventionally pretty. She had, I remember, darkish brown hair with a sort of band of blonde hair across the top of it. Why, goodness only knows. But it was an indisputably feminine touch. Her figure was, and is, slim and her voice suggested, and still suggests, that at any moment it would break into a chuckle, which it frequently did. She gave the impression that she was pleased to talk to me. If this was not so, it was a familiar and a perfectly legitimate exhibition of feminine charm.

She has a touch of the *gamine*, of cockney impudence, about her, for she is London bred and born. Her voice is the perfectly natural voice of the woman of the world, and she is as graceful off the stage as she is on it. Never has her success gone to her head, and those who know her personally better than I do tell me of her domestic side— her passion for cookery and her devotion to her charming grown-up daughter, herself just embarking on a stage career. If she shows half her mother's brilliance she will pass many a comrade on the road to Mecca and may rest well contented.

When two people have impressed themselves indelibly on one's mind it is almost impossible not to let thoughts flit pleasantly from one to the other—and as I think of my Lady I hark back to my Lord—for Coward talks as wittily as he writes. One of the classic remarks to his credit, which had he made it would have been Gilbert at his best, was his admonition to a well-known actress who had returned from Germany, where she had been undergoing a cure for diabetes. Happily recovered, she was in a somewhat over-critical mood one evening, and insisted on firing shafts haphazard at all and sundry. Nothing stopped her until at last Mr. Coward whispered to her in his most ingratiating manner, " My dear, no one is more delighted than I am that you have returned to us strong and well, with your diabetes a thing of the past—but do you think it quite fair to be so cruel. Surely you shouldn't add insulin to injury."

But here I am, wandering away from a beautiful lady, a thing not even a post-war gentleman should do—not, indeed, mind you, forgetting her for a moment, for this will never be, dear Gertrude Lawrence, but just wandering, that's all, in remembering your partner, whom you worked with so divinely. America has claimed you for the time being, but don't stay away too long, for our theatre needs you, and your public aches to see their Gertie once again, and though not for publication may I echo—I do, too.

# GRACIE FIELDS

"Our Gracie!" Everyone who knows her, it seems, and millions who do not, delight in referring to the vastly popular Miss Gracie Fields in this possessive fashion; and whether they come from Lancashire or Devonshire, from Rochdale or Rochester, from Wigan or Chelmsford or Aberdeen, they will almost invariably add, with as good a shot at the accent as may be, " Eh, laad, but she's champion. Bah goom, she's awreet!"

It is impossible not to refer to Gracie Fields in this homely fashion, which she would certainly prefer, for she is the very personification of that simple domestic humour which can bring her in the simple domestic income of anything between £80,000 and £100,000 a year.

No comedienne has been worshipped as " our Gracie " is worshipped since the days of "our Marie"—Marie Lloyd. But Gracie Fields' appeal is much wider. She has only to step on the stage after a long absence or a short one and say, " Gee, bah goom, it's good to be 'ome!" and the audience is in the hollow of that hand which once worked for a pittance in a mill.

Gracie Fields must be the only music-hall " star " whom a Lord Chief Justice has, at his own express desire, watched while at her work. My friend, Lord Hewart, said in an after-dinner speech : " It would be a great honour for a Lord Chief Justice to meet a lady who, I believe, earns more in one night than one of His Majesty's Judges gets in a year." The sequel to that speech was that Lord and Lady Hewart went to Ealing, where Gracie Fields was working on a film, and had tea with her in the studio. Photographers pounced on them, of course. The Lord Chief adopted an attitude of dignified repose. "Nay, nay, laad," said Gracie, "we've got to get busy and talk about summat!" And it was so. We must remember they are fellow Lancastrians.

She had undertaken to do some electioneering for Mr. Ramsay MacDonald at Seaham and to speak for him. She sent him a telegram : "Hope we shall both be successful in our work and be able to sit back and say, 'Thank heaven for the British public.' Good luck, and may you, the best man, win."

She has confessed that the secrets of her astounding success are looking on the bright side of things and making fun of the rich. Which means that she must now make fun of herself, for she is very rich. But that she has always done. Yet her pride in her humble origin, her love for the poor, and her hatred of the ostentatious side of wealth, is sincere and at the same time devoid of that perverted form of snobbery—you know the self-made millionaire who says, "I'm not a gentleman, thank God!" which is even more irritating than the ordinary type.

A friend once met her when Gracie was suffering from a severe cold, and told me how she had caught it. She had an engagement at a music-hall up north, and it was, of course, packed. Two or three thousand people were gathered in the street, unable to get a seat, and it was a chilly, wet night. So Gracie went out into the rain in her flimsy stage frock and sang "Sally" to them.

"You don't have to sing to them, Gracie," said her manager.

"Heck!" she replied (she is always saying "Heck!"), "maybe these folk will never get another chance to see me. It may give them a bit of happiness." This was, I am sure, neither conceit nor showmanship. It was just kindness.

She gets between 4,000 and 5,000 letters a week, I am told, and most of the writers want something.

She has, as we all know, a remarkable voice, with which she delighted to play very unoperatic tricks—a sort of yodel which her audience love—" codling," I believe she calls it. But she was almost persuaded to take her voice seriously by no less a person than Tetrazzini! Tetrazzini was in a box listening to her performance and met her in her dressing-room afterwards, full of warm-blooded Italian embraces and congratulations. "When I was a kid," said Gracie, "I said that one day I would try to become a second Madame Patti. But it will have to be a second Tetrazzini now."

" Beating the drum! " is considered a constant and even necessary habit in the show business. Gracie Fields is surely the only actress to get inside it. But a different sort of drum. She was once taking a party of visitors to the Plaza, Dublin, where the Irish Sweepstake was being drawn. Having a big bump of curiosity, she left her party to inspect at close quarters the huge cylindrical "drum" in which the fateful counterfoils are whirled about. For some odd reason, she decided to look at the interior. Meanwhile a member of the main party wanted to see how the thing worked, and asked an official to set it in motion. As it started to revolve, a scream was heard from within. The machine was instantly stopped and from it emerged a dazed and bedraggled Gracie. " Ah feel like a stoofed doock! " she said when she had recovered her breath.

Rochdale and Hollywood are a good many miles apart in more senses than one. Gracie Fields in Hollywood preserved stubbornly all her North Country individuality —she could not shed it if she tried—and the home of all that is glamorous and exotic (and rather absurd) liked her for it. Perhaps a touch of a wet street in Wigan is refreshing after ceaseless Californian sunshine.

She met Charlie Chaplin.

" Charlie Chaplin couldn't place me," she said on her return. " He had never seen me in England, you know. He seemed to have some idea that I was Happy Fanny Fields. So he asked a friend what my ' turn ' was like. They said I was a bit like Marie Dressler and sang the same sort of songs as Grace Moore. So then Charlie told his Chinese cook to serve roast beef and Yorkshire pudding for my benefit, and we sang ' Boiled beef and carrots ' as a duet. Shirley Temple, she confesses, frightened her. " She fastened me with her bright little eyes, and I knew I would have to be on my best behaviour, or she would trip me up."

" Our Gracie " is fond of all sorts of pets, and had at one time four Airedale dogs, whom she called Dismal, Misery, Old Bill and Desmond, a canary called Cuthbert, and a parrot named Mac. At various periods she has owned monkeys, geese, and bears, and in South Africa she had a narrow escape from death from a puff-adder which she did not own.

Whether in Chelsea, Capri or Rochdale, on the stage of the Palladium or in a film studio, she is always the same cheerful, sturdy, unaffected Gracie Fields—emphatically " awreet." As I pen these words I hear this World Favourite has received a well-deserved honour. Hurrah !

Alf had met our Gracie on several occasions and endorsed every word his friend the author had said about her, indeed, he would have been a jackass if he hadn't, and he then wondered what he should find in the little Tabloid of Tallulah, whom he had known almost from the day she set foot in hospitable England.

# TALLULAH BANKHEAD

"You are wonderfell! You are more wonderfell than ever you were."

It was to Miss Tallulah on a first night that this was shouted from the gallery by an enthusiastic admirer. It has been a catch phrase ever since—but as I say it was the charm of the Bankhead that caused it to be coined.

She is, or was when she was the centre of much hysterical adulation in the London she has deserted for the past three years, the impersonation of what every woman in the gallery (and not only in the gallery) would like to be. It is the romantic dream, made manifest, of women whose lives lack romance. They worship her personality. They gasp at the clothes she wears, and gasp still more when she takes them off on the stage—and there was a time when it was an error for her to appear in any play in which there was not a disrobing act. These women loved to see her in theatrical situations which involved her in glamorous and adventurous journeys to Paris, New York, Le Touquet or the South of France. And before taking their own non-glamorous and unadventurous journeys to the suburbs by bus or tube, they would wait on a wet pavement outside the stage-door to shout, "Tallulah, you're *wonderfell*."

I am not decrying this type of idolatry, for all its hysteria. Better far for the stage to have too much of it than none at all. Nor do I suggest that Miss Bankhead is not in many respects wonderful just because that catchword has been used so often in circumstances with which the highest standards of criticism do not go hand-in-hand. For no personality, however exotic, and no beauty, however compelling (and this charming lady has both) can do the trick unassisted by brains and considerable aptitude for the actress's job.

I once saw Tallulah give an uncannily clever imitation of Sarah Bernhardt. It was one of her "parlour tricks," and probably the best of them. That does not, of course, automatically put her into the Bernhardt class or anywhere near it. But it does mean that she has a quality. The fact that her beauty, her uncommon voice, the "sex-appeal" parts she was condemned, or chose, to play, brought fame too quickly—she hardly served any apprenticeship—may have brought mistakes at the same time. Yet she was never a fake. She had talent and more than talent. And she worked hard.

Her hard work on the stage and her conscientiousness at rehearsals were the more praiseworthy in that she played hard off it. Perhaps too hard. I met Tallulah Bankhead several times away from her work and found her, as indeed she was, a most amusing and happy companion. The wild heroine of late parties, about whom so much has been written, I never met. I would not say that no one has ever met her; but I am convinced that if one cut down those stories which were all over London a few years ago of Tallulah's revels, etc., to one-tenth, one might get at something like the truth. Certain sections of the press cultivated tales of Tallulah and adorned and elaborated them. By the time they were passing round by word of mouth they were exaggerated to a degree of ludicrous and unbelievable absurdity. But people did believe them, and, what is more, I do not think the " heroine " of them minded very much whether they were believed or not.

For that reason, although she rarely—if, indeed, ever—did outrageous things, she was supremely contemptuous of public opinion. There is nothing loud or vulgar about her —she comes from a well-known Southern family and her father (from whom she obviously gets her good looks) is Senator Bankhead of Alabama—and off the stage she is quietly, and sometimes carelessly, dressed. She does not deck herself out with jewels. She is as natural as a kitten. That she is quite as likely to call a taxi-man " darling " as her closest friend does not mean that she is insincere. " Darling " is just a word which that husky voice of hers has to utter in every other sentence.

She is good nature itself, generous to a fault, and would not hurt anyone's feelings for the world. She eats very little, mostly at the wrong time. She smokes too many cigarettes and admits it. " Give me a cigarette and my lipstick and I am happy," I heard her say. " They are the only things I cannot do without."

A few years ago she was probably the most widely discussed woman in London, and not only in theatrical circles, she came after the days of picture postcard beauties ; had she not, picture postcards of Tallulah Bankhead would have been sold daily by the ton. But her portrait was painted by Augustus John, which is rather more important. This portrait used to hang in the flat she had in a mews off Farm Street, and caused almost as much discussion as its subject. Art critics were on the whole unfavourable. " A lifeless woman " they called it. " Eyes like a fish . . . a pale pink ghost . . . Elongated and sharp-chinned " were among sundry other epithets. Tallulah herself adored it, and adored it sincerely. "Perhaps they think I'm ugly," she said. "Well, some people do and they're right. Some people think I'm beautiful. They're right, too. It's a question of taste. Anyway, it's not a chocolate box picture. Oh, darling, fancy me as a chocolate box picture!"

Of Miss Bankhead in connection with pictures of another type I can say nothing. I have never seen any of her films, though at one time I used to read of her as a possible rival to the Garbo or the Dietrich. Why she has not since justified those predictions I do not know. She is at least as beautiful as either and rather like both. So perhaps one day she will.

Her best performance, in my opinion, was in "They Knew What They Wanted," a drama at the St. Martin's Theatre, in which she played the wife of a doting Italian husband, much older than herself, played by the late Sam Livesey. Her pathos, tenderness and restraint were as true as they were, at that time, surprising—at least to me. To regard her, as some still do, as a sort of gifted amateur, forced into the limelight and big parts by a strong personality and an exciting off-stage existence, is nonsense; and unfair nonsense at that.

Her gift for comedy is equally genuine, and no one could have got more value out of the impudently witty lines of Noel Coward's "Fallen Angel" at the Globe Theatre over twelve years ago. So Tallulah Bankhead was no mere flash in the pan. In that play, I recall, someone had to say to her, "My dear, you're all unhinged!" "Thank you," she replied, "I'm perfectly hinged!" These lines may not seem in cold print masterpieces of humour, but their effect on the audience, for a large part of which the actress herself must be given credit, was electrical. In the jargon of the profession, they "stopped the show."

# FAMOUS LADIES OF THE STAGE

At one time I remember it was mooted that she intended to play Ophelia, and on being asked by an interviewer if it was really true that she might possibly appear in " Hamlet," she very wittily said, " Yes, darling, I've been thinking of doing so for a long time, but I can't make up my mind whom I shall get to play with me. Now to begin with, tell me, darling, whom ought I to cast for the First Gold-digger."

Come back, Tallulah ! It would be really refreshing to hear the gallery call out again : " You are more wonderfell than ever you were."

# ANNA PAVLOVA

Adeline Genee was the most wonderful dancer I ever saw. I do not mean for a moment to set myself up as an expert critic of the terpsichorean art, but I am entitled to shout the name of Genee as loudly as they used to at the old Empire, for I have not only seen her in ballet proper but in Empire ballet spectacles such as "Round the Town," in which this remarkable lady set herself to dance in nearly every style, excelling in them all.

In face and figure she was of the distinctly virile school, and I cannot imagine any artist either before her day or to come who could infuse such sweetness and such strength into all her characterizations—and they were many—as did the divine Genee of the Twinkling Feet and Perfect Poise.

Anna Pavlova one watched in ecstasy, and when in the arms of Mordkin, these two incomparable artists seemed to me to be suspended 'twixt earth and sky. Her "Swan" remains for ever a picture painted in a golden frame of memory, a thing impossible to forget, a thing for a rival impossible of capture.

Pavlova was known, for the most part, as a bright and lonely star—lonely, that is to say, except for a succession of partners. She appeared for a short time in Paris with the late Serge Diaghileff, as a "guest artist" as it is called. She was a success, but the association was inevitably doomed to be a short one. Both were great artists, and both, therefore, had more than a due share of egotism.

Diaghileff was mainly interested, moreover, in the effect

of his ballets as a whole, paying much attention to music, *décor*, story, etc. Pavlova saw the thing much more simply. To her a ballet was pre-eminently a matter for the dancers, and for the star dancer—herself—at that. In short, Diaghileff did not believe in the " star " system and Pavlova did.

My reason for this possibly technical discourse on ballet in general, on which I do not, as I have said, pretend to be in any degree an expert—I am only, in a mild and very occasional way, a spectator—is that it helps to indicate the character of Pavlova, whom I met on many occasions and of whom I was a fervent admirer. For the greatest dancer of her generation (some say the greatest dancer the world has ever known) was an extremely simple person. She was a woman of one idea, and that was her art. She would tolerate mediocrity in all else around it on the stage, but never in dancing itself. She set an immensely high standard, the standard she had reached herself, and expected her pupils and associates to attain to it. And she could be, to say the least of it, impatient when they did not. And how could they ? In addition to her natural genius, she had the capacity for hard work, which she demanded in others. Hard work paid her well, for she left £100,000.

She had had a hard struggle since the night in February, 1893, when she had watched the audience enter the famous Maryinsky Theatre in St. Petersburg and, a small, dark-eyed child, had determined to be a dancer. For her father had died when she was two, and she was living with her mother in one tiny room. At eight she entered the academy which trained the Imperial Troupe of Dancers, under the patronage of the Tsar himself. Discipline was strict and the meals meagre. But one day the Tsar (Alexander III) paid a visit and kissed little Anna Pavlova. In 1905 she left the Maryinsky Theatre, where she had become one of the principal dancers, and five years later she came to the Palace Theatre, London.

It was there that I first met her and her partner Mordkin (with whom she had a sensational quarrel in public). She was a slim, yellow-faced girl, not in the least conventionally beautiful, and without her make-up and stage costume, almost plain. But her face had a strange and rather ethereal quality and I could not but notice that her legs, instead of being plump with muscle, as are those of the majority of ballet dancers, were slender and exquisitely shaped. My friend, Herman Finck, then the *maestro* of the Palace Theatre, conducted for her, and it was not long after, liking London as much as London liked her, that she took the house at Golders Green, Ivy Lodge, which was to be her permanent home for a number of years in spite of her ceaseless wanderings in many corners of the world.

Here she gave interesting garden parties, which I occasionally attended. I remember they were rather formal affairs and a top-hat and a morning coat were considered *de rigueur* for men. One met plenty of people one knew and Madame played hostess in semi-queenly fashion. She had enormous dignity as well as grace, and although she was never, I think, vain, she was conscious of her position at the very summit of her profession. After greeting her, one wandered round the very lovely grounds, watched the swans which were her pets, and inspected the house, one room of which was surrounded with mirrors and practice bars and cupboards stacked full of little pink dancing shoes.

" I have five cygnets for which I want to find good homes," Pavlova said to me at one of these parties; " but I must feel certain that they will be most carefully trained."

" How does one train a cygnet ? " I asked.

" With patience and faith in God's help," she said.

This somewhat startling reply was meant in all solemnity. I could never quite make out whether Pavlova had a sense of humour or not. Perhaps it was a Russian sense of humour. But here she was simply giving a quiet, if odd, example of her piety, which was deep and sincere. When she left Ivy Lodge on her travels she would always bless it, a custom of members of the Church to which she belonged.

And how extensive were those travels! She visited, as I have said, practically every part of the civilized globe and many parts which knew not civilization as we know it. In California she was a great favourite with the film colony. Hollywood took to her instantly, both as a woman and as an artist, and Charlie Chaplin became one of her many friends. Posterity should be grateful, and also those alive now who never had the good fortune to see Pavlova, that some films were made of her dancing.

At intervals she would return to London, and live in semi-retirement at Ivy Lodge, working away at clay-modelling, which had become her hobby. She had married some years before M. Dandré, who had been her accompanist. She pottered about her garden, talked to her swans and read the suggestions for ballets which were sent to her by the dozen. But I do not think she ever accepted one.

On several occasions Pavlova made certain English musicians angry by attacking fiercely English art, or, rather, what she deemed to be the lack of it. " England had no art," she declaimed, as a preliminary thump of the drum before one of her last Covent Garden seasons. " Your country is in a dreadful state artistically. You have no opera, no drama, no orchestra—except Sir Henry Wood's orchestra, and that is of the people, and great art cannot come from the people."

We must remember that Pavlova was a product of Imperialist Russia, though after this such a reminder is hardly necessary. As for ourselves, it is only necessary to say that Pavlova was wrong.

With her opinion of American jazz music, which has now spread everywhere like a blight, more will be found to agree. " To me," she said in the last years of her life, " jazz is the very lowest form of amusement, and one for which I have nothing but the most supreme contempt. It is entirely without beauty ; its music a horrible noise made by raucous instruments, giving forth only savage rhythm."

Incompetence in teaching her own beloved art she attacked even more fiercely. She had been asked to a certain dancing academy to give her opinion on a pupil's performance. She gave it. " Here there is no talent and a method which is wholly wrong." Then, turning to the head teacher, she said : " I consider it utterly disgraceful that you even should have presumed to teach dancing. Not only are you incompetence personified, but you are spoiling years of these children's lives. And now will some one please conduct me to my car."

Pavlova was at work to the very end. She caught a chill during a season at the Hague in January, 1931, and died in her sleep.

The nearby village clock had just heralded the hour of nine and Alf, having only waded through half of his friend's book of pleasant memories, shouted for his man to get him a taxi as the office waited and the " leader " must not be late.

To pass the last five minutes before dashing off to the ink which had to be splashed for the benefit of a penny public, he glanced at the last chapter of Famous Ladies of the stage to read of

# SARAH BERNHARDT

I HAD the honour of knowing this mighty actress, but only slightly. It would be as ridiculous of me to discuss her art ungenerously as it would be for a pavement artist to criticise Rubens. I lay my homage at the feet of genius and write only of things I know and things I remember of a woman whose life was as varied and extraordinary as that of our own Edmund Kean.

I first met her on the stage of the Adelphi Theatre when for the first time she played Hamlet in London. If it wasn't Hamlet it certainly was a *tour de force* on the part of the divine Sarah. I stood in the wings all the evening, and Shakespeare's verse in French fell strangely on the ear, " *Hélas ! pauvre Yeorick, je le connais bien 'Oratio !* " seemed very odd to hear, and " Omelette " for " Hamlet " to me savoured more of the kitchen than the battlements.

I remember during the graveyard scene it was amusing to see the great actress turn her back to the audience and urge on the supers frantically, saying, " *Allez ! allez ! Vite ! vite !* " They were a gang of cockneys in monk's habits, who hadn't the remotest idea what she was talking about.

First impressions are not always infallible. I saw Duse play Camille, and I thought that no one in the world could equal, much less eclipse her in the part. She was especially wonderful in the last act where, discovered in bed dying of consumption, she had covered her head with the pillows and seemed in her restless weakness to gain strength by shifting them hither and thither as she spoke. It was not long afterwards that I saw Bernhardt, and almost against my will I was vanquished. Great though Duse was, her French rival was infinitely greater. She was Paris itself. Her midnight was indeed her midday, and her recital of her lover's last letter, instead of reading it as all other Camilles had done, was tragedy in it highest flights. Poor soul! In her agony of mind she had tried to gather comfort by reading it over and over again till the words, having burned themselves into her brain, and stamped themselves on her heart, sought escape mechanically through two parched lips.

Many years passed before I was destined to appear on the same bill with her at the Coliseum. She gave an excerpt from Rostand's *L'Aiglon*, for which she was receiving £800 a week (her contract, by the way, calling for a proportion of that sum to be paid her every evening before the curtain rose). No longer was she the Sarah of the sinuous body, whose horsewhip had justly punished a critic who had libelled her. She had grown very stout, and her face, once as delicate as a spring flower, had become massive, so much so in fact that as she stood talking to me in her dressing-room, tunicked in the white uniform of the eaglet, it was difficult not to suppose she was a man. She spoke in French, asking me if I would accept a souvenir of our meeting. I thanked her, but refused to accept her charming offer, but on her pressing me to choose something, however, I begged for a button from her coat. At once she ordered her maid to cut one off. The woman looked daggers at me, but smiled when I slipped a five-pound note into her hand.

It has been said that the French are always either in black or a bad temper. This may be so, but who is there who can deny that money has always made French women show their pretty teeth?

On my taking leave of this actress of a century, she placed in my hand a little silver box which held the dry rouge she was accustomed to make up with and insisted on my accepting it.

To the sorrow of the universe, one of her legs had been amputated at this period, and at every performance she had to be carried from her dressing-room to the stage in an invalid's chair. One night as she was being taken to the scene in which she appeared (and in which she sat throughout the playlet) she passed two dancing girls who had just finished their turn. With great courtesy she said, " *Bon soir, Mesdemoiselles,*" to which they replied cheerily, " Rumbo, and you ? " They meant no disrespect. As a matter of fact, I don't suppose her name conveyed anything to them.

Apart from the admiration the whole world gave her, she was greatly loved. Her dressing-room was always crowded with visitors, and more often than not these receptions caused the curtain to be kept down as long as half an hour. The only time I had the honour of supping with her was at Nottingham. She came to the theatre there to give two special performances. The piece she appeared in was over at eleven. The meal was ordered for 11.30. At twelve she reached the hotel and at once took a hot bath, and, having dressed, returned to the sitting-room, supper not being served till one. She retired for the night at 2.30, fresh and young in spirit.

From the hour that she left the convent where as a child she appeared in charades and simple little plays to the day of her death she lived in a maelstrom of publicity, attacking and attacked, triumphant with her public, often at war with her critics ; and in her private life a stormy petrel endeavouring to chart the waters of a turbulent world. Early in her career she slapped the face of one of the women stars of the Comedie Française, because at a soirée this lady had pushed her little sister against a pillar for having trodden by accident on her dress. Her battle of life had commenced ; one in which she was always in the trenches with seldom a visit to a camp of rest.

To describe her as *unusual* would be to greatly understate the case, for she was a law unto herself. As an example, has anyone but Bernhardt ever thought of sleeping in a coffin—and yet this was very often her habit. For some time this curious piece of furniture, fashioned in ebony, lined with white satin, had been the great attraction in the *entresol* in the Rue de Rome. Expecting one day to be placed in it for her last sleep, she sometimes lay in it to rehearse, as it were, for her last part. She even had herself photographed in it, lying in a shroud, with closed eyes and arms crossed, with palms and flowers on her winding sheet and candles at her side. When the great actress did die the coffin had become too shabby to be used, so another one was ordered.

Her love of wild animals was abnormal, and she at times had almost a menagerie. During one of her visits to England she journeyed to Liverpool to buy two lion cubs. When on her arrival she found that they had been sold she bought instead a cheetah and a wolf.

The number of performances given by Sarah Bernhardt can, I think, never have been exceeded by any artist at any time, as she not only acted all over the world, but acted all the time. Indeed, a statistician calculated that she was so fond of suicide in her plays that she had thrown herself into the Seine over ten thousand times, and had shot herself five thousand times.

Damala, whom she married, was a Greek, and a confirmed dope fiend; indeed, during his last illness it was
never understood how he had managed to obtain the drugs
which were found in his room after his death. Bernhardt
herself took drugs during the greater part of her life. Not in
the same way, nor of the same kind as did Damala. She was
a martyr to headaches and suffered from sleeplessness, and
so took not only sleeping potions, but aspirins as well. After
her leg was amputated, a tragic happening which occurred
towards the end of her long life, the pain still remaining,
to relieve it she very often took three or four phials of some
form of narcotic a day. This alone was enough to kill her;
how it did not do so those around her marvelled.

Bernhardt may have hated the majority of dramatic critics,
many of whom were merciless towards her throughout
her career, but her hatred of the Germans, having, as she had,
lived through the war of 1870, was an obsession. Time
passed, however, and when she ultimately appeared in Berlin,
and won over audiences who knew what her innermost
feelings were about their country, and were therefore anything but inclined to welcome her, when she conquered
them as an artist and was received in everything she did with
frenzied applause, her attitude towards France's former
enemies changed. She realized that any individual who
could sway a concourse of people might become an
ambassador for good or evil, and she elected to become the
former. However, she again changed her mind, for when
in 1914 war was made upon the land of her birth by its former
foes, all her old passionate hatred was aroused afresh, and
if anything was redoubled, to think that again she was to hear
the thunder of German artillery at the gates of her beloved Paris.

As a slip of a girl she was not only thin, but as Dumas

has said, " as thin as a broomstick." Though we nearly all
change with the years, it seemed impossible that the dominat-
ing, almost portly old lady was ever the ethereal being that
created Phèdre and La Tosca. Her adherents were legion,
and I suppose as a natural corollary it is no matter for surprise
that she had many enemies who never ceased to invent or
exaggerate. At one period it was given out that she masquer-
aded as a man, a thing that was utterly untrue. On her first
appearance in London at the old Gaiety in 1879 she suffered
from stage fright, but notwithstanding this her triumph
was complete and she became the rage.

It is never recorded of her that she was jealous of her
rivals. The consciousness of her great powers no doubt
saved her from this most devastating of all human weaknesses.
Indeed, she even placed her own theatre at the disposal of
celebrated foreign actors—such as Irving, Ellen Terry and
even Duse. She declared that she wanted to let her public
whom she adored see the most distinguished representatives
of foreign art acting in her playhouse. The undoubted
success of Duse did not trouble her in the slightest. As the
years rolled on, no longer had she to defend her reputation.
The scandals ceased and the French public accepted the
actress as she was and had become accustomed to her vagaries.
Her one object in her later years was to defeat old age, and
to do this she surrounded herself with all that was youthful
in art, and she recovered all the happiness of adolescence
on the night of her triumph as L'Aiglon. This may be said
to have been the summit of her career.

During the Great War her thoughts were entirely of the
wounded, for whom she performed continually, sometimes
as often as twice a day, and she was heard many a time to
say : " I have acted before kings, I have been applauded by

the public of every country, I have known the most wonderful evenings, but I have forgotten them all—I only remember my life behind the lines."

For many, many years of her life she had a loving and charming man at her side in the person of her son Maurice. It was in the last days of March, 1923, that the spirit of this tremendous actress, probably the greatest tragedienne the world has ever known, was released from a body that had suffered much. Not only France but the whole world mourned her. She was laid to rest in the cemetery of Père La Chaise. That " one becomes famous only after death " was one of her beliefs. In her case this was not true. For during her lifetime she was an idol that was worshipped by a world that was ever prostrate before her genius.

There were many other famous ladies written of in Semorix's little book, several of whom, indeed, Alf himself had often acclaimed in print, among them being—he noticed as he hastily turned the leaves before putting the volume in his pocket—the delicious Lilian Braithwaite, who has made more bad lines sound like good ones than any woman who ever trod the stage ; a long appreciation of Edith Evans in classic comedy and of her exquisite delivery of Rosalind's epilogue ; the power and tremendous theatre sense of Flora Robson ; while coupled with the magic comedy of Ellis Jeffreys and Irene Vanbrugh, he saw tribute paid to her sister Violet ; the genius of Cicely Courtneidge and Binnie Hale ; and the bewildering brilliance of Ivy St. Helier ; and, amongst many others, last but by no means least, there was much of Margaret Rawlings, who surely must be the coming tragedienne of our day, thought Alf, for no one he mused, who heard her say, " O, God ! Oh, God ! Oh,

God ! " as Parnell lay dead in her arms can surely doubt this ; vital and brilliant, direct and unafraid, with a voice that flings challenge in its every tone—this, so the critic gleaned, is what the humble author felt was the stuff with which Margaret Rawlings's theatre sisters of bygone days compelled audiences to listen and shout their approbation.

By an odd coincidence, as Alf dashed along in his taxi towards that quarter of London so aptly described as the Road of Scoops and Scurry—otherwise Fleet Street—whom should he see but his friend Semorix himself. Obviously, thought Alf, my actor friend has sat up all night to keep an early morning appointment. They waved to each other and managed, as Alf's driver found himself in a traffic jam, to fix up an appointment for luncheon on the following day. "It will be my duty, I hope not a painful one," said Alf, "to criticise your split infinitives this week."

"Thank you, old fellow," said the gentleman who had imposed upon a confiding Public for fifty years by pretending to be some one on the stage and nobody in particular off it. "I trust you will look upon my effort with a kindly eye." "Mercy shall be tempered with Justice," replied Alf. "But how many more women you could have written about—and you haven't."

"I know all about that," said the amateur ink-slinger, "but the number of sweet and brilliant ladies who have honoured me with their friendship is legion, so to write of them all would be impossible, especially as I understand the price of paper is going up daily ! "

# PART III

## TALK, IDLE TALK

SEMORIX had kept the appointment with Alf and the meal
had passed off pleasantly enough, the actor being by no means
surprised that while the journalist seemed knowledgable
enough about the Art of the Theatre, from a highbrow point
of view, he seemed delightfully ignorant of the players'
technique or the practical difficulties with which the playhouse
is faced at every turn.

" I have often wished I had been an actor," said Alf.

" So have I," smiled his guest.

" Why do you say that ? You have been successful enough."

" My dear fellow," said the author of the Tabloid
Biographies of Famous Ladies, " don't talk about *success*,
say rather that I have not been found out. Please put my
contribution to the Art of acting little higher than that,
for, believe me, no one is more alive to the fact than myself
that I am a Jack of many Trades and only a half-master of
one. As to success, if I dared even for a moment to imagine
that I had merited praise, my sleep would be as full of torment
as was Richard's restless hour upon the eve of Bosworth
Field. Remember, my friend, that I have watched many
great ones and if I were to forget the heights from which
they beckoned me, their accusing voices would swear
vengeance on the head of one, who, if he be possessed of
nothing else, at least has sense enough to know how far
he falls below the standards of the Masters at whose feet
he tried to learn his job."

" I don't agree with you," said Alf, " but still, as you

are an expert, I suppose you know best. You have appeared in films, haven't you ? " he continued.

" I have," replied IX, looking a little more than ordinarily vacant.

" Were you good ? " said Alf.

" No, by no means," said IX.

" I should have thought you would have been admirable," ventured Alf, who began to feel he was getting a little out of his depth.

" You are quite mistaken," said the actor, " for as the dry-fly purist is not necessarily a first-class shot, so the film and the stage have nothing whatever to do with one another."

" But surely there are great actors on the screen, aren't there ? " inquired Alf.

" The Screen has given the world no great actors," said IX very decidedly. " Great actors have *gone* to the screen, which is quite another thing, and some of them, either by luck or judgment, have mastered a new technique and applied it to their own. Types there are, of course, who have been discovered and found to be splendid material for this new Art, but they are not actors. To coin a word, they are ' Directorable,' and as such, dance most admirably to a director's tune. But how can they be called artists when they create nothing ? It's true they perform and please in this new world of entertainment, and are much to be applauded, for they help to lighten the lives of an indulgent eager-to-be-made-happy multitude ; but from an Art point of view they must be seen in proper perspective and looked at from one of their own angles, and if this be done they will be found to be only the desired mediums which a creator uses to make his imagination a living thing."

As IX wandered on he became aware that he was talking

Double-Dutch to the famous paragraphist opposite him, and, making an excuse that he had to meet a City Gentleman who he hoped would find money for a new production (but as the piece was not a musical comedy he was not sanuigne of achieving this end) he rose and Alf followed him.

Bowed out as they had been bowed in by that prince of his profession, the famous Santorelli, they made their way to the cloakroom, so called because no such thing as a cloak had ever reposed there, where they fell in with many of the best known men about town—faces, which, as they say in the Press, " make news." To the right was one of the nicest men of Alf's acquaintance, who had made history by giving his name to a special menu and, by calling it *à la carte*, had earned the grateful thanks of all who understand that mass production for the epicure is a thing to be avoided.

To the left was Noel Curtis-Bennett explaining to a millionaire with writer's cramp and a wooden foot what wonderful things are the Playing Fields of Britain, for which he works day and night. And so they are, and so is he.

Sitting at a table in the window was one of the grandest Englishmen, the late Mr. Bertram Mills, who deserved so well of his generation and his country, which he always served with both hands.

And among the many whom Alf knew and was fond of, there was no one he admired more than Louis Greig, who has placed a by no means easy-to-eradicate footprint on the sands of England. Alf was thankful for his friendship, for he knew him to be not only John Bull in excelsis, but in addition he had the priceless faculty of being able to make the sun shine on a dark day, and indeed on one occasion had made Alf extremely happy by convincing Alf that Alf was the author of a book which Alf had only read—a great and precious gift this. How jolly it would be, thought Alf, if some of the Lord Dulldrearys would also try and become the Second Gentlemen of Europe.

As he sat at dinner that night discussing with Edward the luncheon he and Semorix had had together, and the quite interesting points of view on the Theatre Topics that had arisen as they munched smoked salmon, made more smoky by the ladies' cigarettes, which were labelled Virginian, so that maid and matron might start from scratch, Edward asked Alf if the men and women whose names are household words and with whom he knew Alf often came in contact, were difficult people to get on with.

" What, the really big ones ? " said Alf. " Good heavens, no ! As a rule they are simplicity itself, but their secretaries and hangers on, the barnacles on the bottoms of the great ships, are not people you would borrow money to spend with.

" In fact, I think it is generally these ' Yes-men ' who, being first cousins to the cave dwellers, in decomposing cheeses, are responsible for giving many a false impression of their masters."

" Let me hear about some of them, Alf. Now, by any chance, do you happen to know Somerset Maugham, for instance ? "

" Yes, I do," replied Alf. " Well."

" What a cynic ! " commented Edward.

" In private life, nothing of the sort. He is a most charm- ing and tolerant man, and considering that his inkstand is a well into which he can dip acidly and describe unerringly the failings of those about him, it is something to be thankful for that he flings neither javelin nor poison-tipped dart at the minnows with whom he daily comes in contact.

" Mind you," continued Alf, " I wouldn't pick him as a

man to offend, because before you knew where you were you would probably be pulverised."

"You wouldn't gather that he was a least bit like what you say he is from his books and plays, old fellow, would you?" said the ignorant Edward.

"I wasn't talking about his genius as a writer," replied Alf, "you asked me what he was like to meet. I own that at first I was a trifle frightened of him, for he has what you might describe as a *dangerous* face. His eyes are piercing and his mouth is hard, but I have learned from those who are his intimates and from his attitude to small people like myself that his outward make-up is the cover of a generous and kindly heart. I should say that like many another outstanding figure he is a shy man, though mind you he probably would be the last person to confess it. He is known to his friends as Willie. Some day perhaps I may have an opportunity of introducing you to him. You won't get on very well with him at first as he is epigrammatic in his replies, a most difficult thing to combat, but as the hours go on, unless you bore him, which if you talk rubbish you certainly will, you'll find that the mask will disappear and that he will never make you feel you are the inferior person he knows you to be. Gentle of manner, he has a slight impediment in his speech which to me is extraordinarily attractive, for it keeps you in suspense, waiting for his reply to your question, which you know will be charged with, may I put it, words of ' quality,' so seldom heard in these days of ' You're telling me.'

"And talking of charming and non high-hatted personalities," Alf went on, "one of the kindest of men and one apparently unaware of his great gifts was John Drinkwater.

"On his art, dear fellow," said Alf, assuming for once a humble attitude, "I do not propose to dilate, for the poet is as rare as a kingfisher on a stagnant pond, and into what niche my departed friend (whose loss I greatly deplore) will be placed by the critic in years to come I have not the slightest conception. It is only of him as a man that I permit myself to speak, and this I can do, for I knew him well, and his tragic and unexpected death shocked me beyond words, particularly as only a few hours before he died we spent a late and happy night together at a famous club of which we were both members.

"It was a strange evening and looking back and remembering much that was said in fun and at times tense sincerity, words that fell from his lips were prophetic, for as the hours passed by the poet discussed the Church and defended his unorthodox though deeply religious principles with a determination which brooked no contradiction.

"This particular night commenced with laughter and good humoured chaff. There were only four of us who had forgathered in the lounge. A distinguished actor, an eminent dramatic critic, Drinkwater and myself. As the time wore on it was of course hardly to be wondered at that the tragic abdication of Edward VIII was touched upon and some amusing stories of a famous lady were told.

"On this highly controversial subject Drinkwater expressed no opinion, sitting apart, moody and silent. All of a sudden, however, like summer lightning across a cloudless sky, my friend, whom I thought was little interested in the whys and wherefores of a tragic happening, blurted out angrily, 'The people of this country are all wrong. Time will tell and history will write that the man did well in standing by the woman he loved. He should have been allowed to marry her.' It is needless to say that this bombshell dropped by so distinguished a person in the early hours of the morning, produced a painful silence, for while totally disagreeing with him, it was impossible for us to combat lightly his obviously deep feelings on the matter or dismiss with a jest words which were spoken with ill-concealed pain. We sat and stared, and Drinkwater, finding that the glove he had thrown into the arena seemed unlikely to be picked up by any of us, continued to unburden himself of his belief in the wrong that had been done to a Prince who would have made for England, he said, a great King.

" ' Had he been ousted by a majority ' he went on, ' it would not have altered my views on the subject at all, but no majority ever had a chance of speaking. It was the minority in power who engineered most carefully a complete debacle.'

" On this point, as was only to be expected, three dissenting voices rose angrily, and in a moment we four congenial gentlemen of an hour previously were transformed into people giving and receiving heavy blows. Everything ended happily, however, and I drove him to his home in Hampstead, little thinking that as we bade each other good night we had said good-bye for ever."

A handsome and picturesque figure was John Drinkwater, with his silvery hair and broad-brimmed hat. The son of an actor, he loved the stage and in accents which contained the unmistakable agricultural burr of the Midlands, he would discuss the merits of the mummer, praising with fervour or condemning with a vitality all his own. He loved to act, but he was by no means a good performer. Perhaps he knew this, and being a master in his own art, the fact that he failed to excel in another, was probably to him a thing of little moment. His happy boyish outlook on life was a shield I think given him by Providence to conceal his real lack of humour, for of this he had little, but he was a delightful kindly creature and his large circle of friends live to mourn the passing of a good companion and a very downright English gentleman.

Like all good artists he was very sensitive and never I think quite forgave a critic who wrote of his dramatic work " Cromwell " : " This play is as long as the Cromwell Road and very nearly as dull. . . ." Unfair perhaps, but being a good jest would have been forgiven had John been able to laugh at himself, but this good, honest man neither laughed at his fellows *nor* himself.

" It is curious," said Alf, " that the Cromwell Road seldom seems to be mentioned as a popular place, for even Andrew Lang, when he was asked where he lived, replied, ' walk along the Cromwell Road and when you are dropping dead with exhaustion, you will know you've arrived at my house.' "

" Do you know, Alf," said Edward, " if I were asked whom of all the famous men that have lived during my time I should have liked most to have met, I would without a moment's hesitation reply, ' Henry Irving.' Surely he must have been a most astonishing person."

" Yes, I think you're dead right," said Alf, " for apart from being a mighty actor he must have had a most extra-ordinary personality, from what one gathers of him from the people who knew him in private life. Look at this for instance," said Alf, pushing the evening paper towards his friend, " it's an article written in connection with the centenary of his birth. Not perhaps a great literary effort in itself but at the same time it does go to show that it is very doubtful if any actor of our day will ever make the tremendous impression he did on his contemporaries. Read it and I think you'll agree."

The tribute was headed :

CENTENARY

1838–1938

# TALK, IDLE TALK

Come let us think aloud before the links which bind us to the greater dead are snapped for ever, for then will only hearsay raise its head on high and rob the table of its talk.

## IRVING ! ! ! ! !

From the crash of ocean waves beating against the frowning rocks of grim Tintagel to the voices of little surpliced boys chanting lament at Westminster, is a far cry indeed, but these were the things which heralded a dawn and sang a requiem spanning the days given to the greatest British actor within living memory, indeed perhaps the greatest of any time in the history of our drama, excluding not even the ordered genius of David Garrick, the stately periods of a Kemble, the savage lightning bursts of mighty Kean, the brilliance of intolerant Macready, or the majesty in art of Edmund Phelps. Five beacons these, which lighted Cinderella on her way before the hand of Henry Irving fashioned her in gay brocades and bade her take heart, for he had destroyed the rags of prejudice in which she had been gowned from the first hour that, tinsel-clad, she'd stepped into the kingdom of Shakespeare's make-believe, to sing his verse and so uplift the town.

Henry Irving ! ! !

Proud of the privilege that I knew him well, how truly can I say he was the mightiest actor I have ever seen, and in his art the noblest figure of his day, tremendous and inspiring, comparable only in his varied moods to the wondrous facets of the most precious stone.

To those who saw this man of men, his very name spells magic, and never was a truer summing-up of character than when it was said of him that " Had this great theatre prince chosen to be priest or soldier, the Primate's crown or

Marshal's baton would, without doubt, had he so wished it, have been his own."

Throughout his life, from all his fellows he was a thing apart, and though beyond words kindly to all who came within his orbit, his friendship he gave to few; his love to no one with the exception of his brilliant sons, that perfection of a woman, Ellen Terry, and his life-long confidant John Laurence Toole, though even these I think, had never access to the conscious mind of this devastating and entrancing personality, so seldom were his thoughts trapped into the light of day.

Few are the pictures which do him justice or convey this great tragedian. "The Millais" would be voted weak to a degree if the original were standing by, Whistler's "Philip" by no means the man himself, and it is strange that only photographs taken in later life seem to disclose all that was in his soul when he was young. Happily, however, sculpture seized upon him with success, and gave to us Irving in "Hamlet" and "The Bells" as Irving really was, live and inquiring, a master both of passion and repose. Sensitive of face—how plain to see that the beautiful white hands which he possessed were the outposts of a brain ready for battle; indeed they served him well. Tall and imposing, he had a halting gait and gestures jerky when he emphasized a point, while his voice, though resonant, was oft-times muffled, when wedded to a diction which, more often than not, promoted words of single syllables to two.

From this it might appear to those who'd seek to visualise, that he was grotesque in action. It's true that robbed of his genius he might well have been considered so, but as in his art he was a giant among giants, he dominated his plays, his comrades and his audiences alike and left them in awe and wonderment. In his silences, he made men still. In passion,

### HENRY IRVING

*From the Sculpture by F. Onslow Ford, A.R A., in the Guildhall Art Gallery.*

fearful. When gentle, called up tears and if he smiled the sun shone for the multitude again.

His histrionic power lay not in violent outbursts, but in thought, for he was frail judged by the standard of stronger men, but while in tragic passages he was never loud, no man that I have seen was ever half as terrifying or could convey that fear which Hamlet's father painted for his son. And what a varied gallery was his! As Wolsey, with what dignity superlative did he control a King, and in that courtier's fall, what pathos and despair was his. Sad at ingratitude and uncomplaining to the end. And oh, his gentle Charles, his saintly Becket, and his crimson fiend, tripping and cajoling the new made Faust, even to the Brocken's edge. Who of us that saw these great creations will ever cease to marvel, and then when he cast aside his Mathias and Lesurques, what a comedian could become this iron man, for in his hands Macaire and Jingle were the gayest rogues that ever trod in fact or fiction, creatures made up of arrogance and impudence, barefaced effrontery and conceit.

As theatre man, when shall we ever see his like again? For not only had his vision no horizon, but with his flair, technique and fine unerring touch, he summoned music and the designer's art to weave his dreams into a beautiful reality. Alas! that the pen of Hazlitt knew him not.

And so a hundred years have come and gone since Irving, born of gentle Somersetshire stock, became a saviour of the men and women of his craft whom it was his delight to look upon affectionately and call his comrades. For them he silenced gibe and jest and set his calling on the pedestal he knew it well deserved, and, therefore, thankful though the people were who watched his work and gloried in it, how much more grateful should a profession be to one who, fighting unaided and alone, planted their standard on the top-most height, there to remain for evermore.

" I shall cut that out," said Edward as he finished reading, " it's evidently written by a great enthusiast."

" Obviously."

" When did Irving die ? "

" Nineteen hundred and five at Bradford," replied the encyclopædia. " The last character he ever played was Becket and the last line which fell from his lips as he collapsed at the Cathedral altar was, ' Into Thy hands, O Lord.' A strange coincidence that simulating death as an actor he was in reality dying as a man, for within an hour after the curtain had fallen, Henry Irving breathed his last."

" I suppose you probably met Elgar, didn't you ? " ventured Edward.

" Oh, very often," said Alf, " and anyone more unlike the generally accepted idea of a musician in private life it would have been impossible to conceive. Gentle and courteous to a degree, if you had not known that he was a man whose name will live with those of the great masters, you would have mistaken him for a quiet country gentleman, whose hobby was the rearing of pheasants and his greatest pleasure a tramp over hill and dale with spaniel and labrador as his boon companions. Justly might he have been called the ' well-beloved,' for he had not an enemy in the world. He was an ardent lover of the Turf and, I think I am not wrong in saying that at the Worcester race meeting a fixture had been named after this great son of an historic city to commemorate his affection for the Sport of Kings.

" Age has no terror for me, dear Edward," rambled on Alf, " but the sorrow I feel at the passing of the great who are irreplaceable, add scars that are deep and of which I am for ever conscious."

The journalist having become a trifle leaderish in his soliloquizing, a silence fell upon the pair, which was only broken when a man of their acquaintaince who, still living, must be nameless, passed and with a twitch of his neck wished them an unpleasant good evening.

"That man's as crooked as a ram's horn," said Alf, "and it's a jolly lucky thing for England that he isn't a railway engineer or there wouldn't be a level crossing in the country. In fact, he is such a bad hat that no one dreams of ever signing a contract with him unless they first hold the document up to the light to see if there is an 'if' in the watermark. He is really a horrid fellow, I've known him, man and beast, for twenty years, and in addition to his many doubtful charms he delights in boasting that he is an atheist."

"You do not mean to tell me, my dear Alf, that there are such men?"

"Well, Edward, I often wonder myself. This class of idiot may exist, of course, when all is well with them, but I have grave doubts if anyone has ever seen an atheist in pyjamas with a thermometer registering 105 degrees in his mouth. Talking of these gentlemen of, I am sure, temporary unbelief, I saw an amusing inscription on a tombstone in a Canadian churchyard. It read : 'Here lies an atheist, all dressed up and nowhere to go.'"

### OUT OF TOWN

The silly season had descended on the two friends, bringing with it its usual fight for life, endeavouring as it always does to keep its head above alcohol and water. As the cuckoo is the herald of our rainy summers, so the newspapers are the harbingers of the dull hiatus between the mock hilarity which has passed, and the manufactured gaiety to come. London knows that this silly spell has arrived when, while sipping its morning tea, it reads the leaders in its favourite journals. Mussolini's chin and Hitler's moustache are for the moment forgotten, and in their place are scare headlines as to how to use gas masks should the Swiss navy elect to attack Southend. When the war to come has lost its thrill the newspaper magnates are hard put for copy, and the poor income tax owner is entertained every day with other really important problems, the most vital of them being, " Need film stars marry ? " or " Is true love sex of one and half a dozen of the other ? " both questions, of course, being highly exciting in hot weather.

The leaders on these subjects are Heralds of the Yawn, and Alfred and his friend, being extremely knowledgable, decided now and again to treat London as a billiards table and give it a miss in balk. Occasionally they sort out pastures old, more often than not making their way to Brighton, that best of all seaside resorts, which, owing to the fact that several murders had been committed there during the past year, Edward had christened " The Queen of Slaughtering Places." Edward did not know it well, but to Alf it was a jewel-case crammed full of happy memories. Had Edward known it as I do, thought Alf, to " christen " it would have been about the last thing he would have taken the liberty of doing.

" Victoria, Brighton line ! " shouted Alf, as he jumped into a taxi, followed by the harmless necessary Edward.

" I wonder why it is," said the inquirer on all subjects, " that the whole world is so down upon the Jews."

" Not the British people," said Alf.

" No, perhaps not, but you can't say they are universally loved, are they ? "

# TALK, IDLE TALK

"Well, first of all, old man, I suppose it is that they are cleverer than we Christians."

"Cleverer, or more cunning, do you mean, Alf?"

"Cleverer. It's only the low class Jew that's cunning, and there's very little, to my mind, to choose between the low classes anywhere. It isn't noses that make much difference, because, whether the Jew pokes his into your trousers pocket while he's emptying it—or the Christian looks up at you while he's searching your linings, does not seem to matter much, they're both doing the same thing. But one reason, I think, the Jew is disliked is that if he's common he's much more common than the other common fellow. If he is financially successful he wears his passbook on his sleeve, not necessarily for Jays to peck at, while if he has become powerful he is prone more often than not to invite his opponent to leave the highways for the by-ways, explaining how much more lucid he can be in the Maze at Hampton Court. Everyone, dear Edward, is entitled to dislike the particular Jew who has done him a real bad turn or who has torn the shirt off his back in wintry weather. But to be down on a community because of a few individuals seems to be not only an extremely unchristianlike proceeding, but the height of folly. After all, it is tantamount to saying to the Creator that you are extremely annoyed with Him for having fashioned a gentleman who can talk with his hands and lisp at the same time. Besides, neither of these two accomplishments are copyright, and being by no means difficult to imitate, surely the handicap is not excessive. Of course, if it is the question of Creed that causes your gorge to rise, there is one very easy way to straighten that out. Hop into your own place of worship next Sunday and maybe you will hear something about loving your neighbour as yourself."

" My dear fellow," said Edward, " don't hand me out instructions. I was, if you remember, only asking you a simple question beginning with ' I wonder why ' . . . Personally, I entirely agree with you. Throughout my life many of my dearest friends have been of the Jewish Faith, and anything like their kindness and generosity it would be impossible to imagine. So you can count me in as one who has a large corner of his heart filled with many an affectionate memory of hosts of delightful Hebrew friends."

The taxi pulled up at Victoria. As Alf walked up to the ticket office he was brushed aside by sixteen stone of Polish avoirdupois.

" Pole," said Edward.

" Up it," said Alf.

" Return," said the Pole.

" Why ? " said Alf.

" Go to hell," said the Pole.

" Not till you've wired me what it's like," said Alf.

But the hide of the rhinoceros is thick and there are none so blind as those who are determined not to hear. So the Pole had his Pullman ticket politely punched by the porter and went on his way.

> Adding, adding, always adding.
> Multiplying often.
> Subtracting never,
> Just adding, adding, adding.

It was a warm July night. The Palestine Express—with its cars on which notices are displayed, " English spoken here "—bore them and bored them to their destination without mishap other than the shock they received on not hearing any of their immediate neighbours perform acrobatic feats with their H's—or at any rate none at which they could have expressed surprise.

Opposite them a blonde, looking tremendously intelligent —listening attentively to her attendant Donkey—displayed ostentatiously a wedding ring that wouldn't have deceived the night porter of a new block of flats—while not far away a bookmaker with a generous stomach snored heavily— shouting the odds through one nostril and collecting money through the other. The journey, however, was unlike the long trip taken by that celebrated young gentleman who seemed to have delighted in shouting " excelsior " from the housetops, and they found themselves breathing the salted breezes for which Brighton is famed almost before they knew where they were.

" Let us walk," said Alf. " Right," said Edward, " if you can," and as he could, they sent on their things to the hotel by taxi and sauntered from the station along that street from which, if you turn to the left, you will slip on a piece of orange-peel—into charming ornamental gardens.

The residence, once occupied by a Hanoverian gentleman who from all accounts doesn't seem to have troubled to behave like one, especially to his one-time bosom friend George Brummell, a figure by the way who, if he lived to-day, would probably have invented the Forty-shilling suit, spread- eagled itself on their right.

" George IV still seems to haunt this place," said Alf, as they passed the Pavilion. " I wonder what was at the back of his odd mind when he had that house built ? To me it isn't the ghost of George IV which hovers about this town, but a much more attractive one—the ghost of King Harry, dear Harry Preston."

"I agree," said Edward. "I find it hard to believe that he is gone and that we shall never see again that dapper little man, with his big cigar, his smell of eau-de-Cologne, nor feel the 'pull' of his handshake, or hear his invitation to try a glass of 'the old and bold' as he called it, the Golden Vintage which Frank Otter of immortal memory called "Champagne Woine."

"Ah! what a nobleman was Harry, his kindness and hospitality were extraordinary."

"What feasts he gave," recalled Edward. "I remember one of his particularly large banquets preceding one of the big fights. Most of the guests on this occasion *were*, or were reputed to be, men of vast wealth.

"Looking at the millionaires who sat right, left and centre. E. V. Lucas, who was a guest that evening, turned to his neighbour and whispered, 'If ever I have to write dear little Harry's epitaph, and I hope the time for that is far distant, I shall write, " This man sold all that he had and gave to the *rich*!"' E. V. has the best epigrammatic hammer in the world—and goes about hitting golden-headed nails into other men's coffins."

On arrival at their hotel they supped and sat smoking in the hotel lounge, "the one cigarette before turning in" which spun itself into four or five.

"Brighton hotels were different in my grandfather's time," mused Edward. "He was one of the last men, I imagine, to wear a nightcap. Nowadays all we do is to drink 'em."

"Why men wore nightcaps I have never understood. It is said that they were tougher and hardier folk a century ago and that they led a more spartan existence. I wonder? Now we sleep with our bedroom windows open. Then, the bedroom windows were kept shut tight and our grand-fathers and great-grandfathers with three bottles of port inside them, crawled into mahogany four-posters and pulled the bed curtains closely about them. Yet they were usually extraordinarily fit, weren't they ? " asked Edward.

" Yes," replied Alf, " until they fell down in one."

" Hotels were cheaper years ago," said Edward. " Before the War prices went up with a rush. I remember this was touched on in a revue. ' Do you know at some of the Brighton hotels they charge you as much as half a crown for a bath ? ' some one asked. ' I dare say,' came the reply, ' but what's half a crown a week to Sam Lewis ? ' A trifle unkind though, for Sam was a charming little man and always scrupulously well turned out.

" He was that pretty rare specimen, a moneylender with a heart. Under no circumstances would Sam lend money to younger sons—young Guardsmen, or any of the youths about town, who had become temporarily embarrassed and were afraid to tell their parents. On one occasion, and I can vouch for the truth of the story, Mr. Lewis delivered himself of the following to a young gentleman who had cause to regret a visit to Sandown :

" ' No, my boy, I will not lend you any money, the interest I want you couldn't pay and the interest you could pay is no good to me. So here's a hundred pounds as a present, and don't let me ever hear of you trying to borrow money again or I'll tell your father.' "

" It was Sam Lewis who, taking a party with him for a visit to the Continent, on finding himself in Rome grew so weary of its churches and its places of interest (these latter probably reminding him of his office in Cork Street, London) that he gave his friends the slip and went to Monte Carlo alone. He was an inveterate gambler and after having spent a happy night at the tables, wired to his wife, ' You can 'ave Rome.' "

"One more drink," said Edward.

"No," said Alf, for the first time in his life. "We may be spending the week-end on the 'Soused Coast,' but we're not full members yet. Besides, I've work to do to-morrow. Good night."

The two friends slept the sleep of the only just. They would have slept till noon had not that "bitter proclaimer of the rosy dawn," the hotel chambermaid, started her 7 a.m. symphony in the corridor with a full orchestra of cleaning utensils. The chief and solo instrument in what swiftly developed into a concerto, was a vacuum cleaner in B flat, which emitted a low but penetrating drone, sufficient to wake the Seven Sleepers, with a percussion obbligato consisting of bangs on the bedroom door with the business end of a broom and the clanking of pail handles. Occasionally came a scrap of song, "Pail handles I love . . ."

"Why must hotel corridors invariably be cleaned and pressed," grumbled Edward to Alf across a kipper, "at a time when eighty per cent. of the guests are still asleep?"

"To give the remaining twenty the chance to sort themselves out into their proper bedrooms."

"Surely a siren would be simpler?"

"No sirens are simple," replied Alf.

"Now you're trying to be brilliant at breakfast. Wasn't it Wilde who said that only dull people are brilliant at breakfast?"

"Yes; probably he said it at breakfast."

Ten minutes later a walk along the front. Brighton front on a Sunday is now sartorially an affront. Youths sport sportscoats in an attempt to be taken for sportsmen, their padded shoulders, club toes and cuban heels making them look like American prize-fighters out of training. The older males are better dressed and the women are smarter than either. But nowhere is there elegance.

" I suppose I am a little old fogeyish," said Alf, as a cohort of untidiness passed by, " but I can't help wishing that Brighton was as elegant as it used to be. I need hardly say I am not referring to the bucks of the Regency. What I mean is that when I was a youth many people dressed for Brighton as they would dress for Piccadilly. Now they don't dress for either; they just clothe themselves. A top hat in Bond Street in 1938, except during Ascot week or the Eton and Harrow match, is as rare as a Chinaman with red whiskers. As for a top hat in Brighton, you can walk from Hove to Kemp Town and back without seeing one, unless there's a wedding or funeral on, though many of the pedestrians wear three hats during their hours of business. I don't claim any particular virtue for any particular hat or even for convention in dress of any kind. But times have indeed changed. The secret is to change with them. You and I haven't changed altogether. That is why we miss the folk we came to regard as ' characters.' To-day everyone seems to be turned out of the same mould.

" I don't think they're any the worse for that," Alf rambled on. " It is all the result of what we call the march of democracy, and in any march the important thing is to keep in step. Those of us who like to dwell lovingly on what we call the ' good old days,' do so mainly because when we were acquainted with them our capacity for enjoyment was greater. Greater knowledge, longer experience and a development of the critical faculty in consequence, take the edge off the fun, though they compensate in other ways.

" I suppose I had better console myself with the thought that if in this twentieth century a few don't have quite such a good time, the many have a far better time. With all our political difficulties, and with Fascists and Communists clawing and spitting at each other like Kilkenny cats, in the country as a whole there is more general harmony. Whether we shall ever settle down without any wrong notes, like some perfectly rehearsed choral society, is rather doubtful."

" Talking of choral societies," said Edward, " I didn't realise until Sir Thomas Beecham—a genius with a great sense of humour is Sir Thomas—said in a speech recently that there are hundreds of choral societies in England alone. And most of them perform Handel's ' Messiah ' on Good Friday afternoon. Whereby, as they say, hangs a tale— and a true one. A very well-known English tenor, whose speciality is Handel's masterpiece, has a lovely singing voice but speech that should properly accompany the pushing of a barrow of bananas in the Mile End Road. In short, a true ' Gorblimey.' A friend met him in the Strand one Good Friday afternoon. ' Hullo ! ' he said. ' Fancy seeing you out of doors at a time like this. Why aren't you singing in the " Messiah " ? ' ' Yus,' was the reply, ' you've 'it it, you 'ave, and no mistyke. There's Parry Jones a singin' it in the Albert 'All ; Walter Widdop singin' it in Leeds ; and Joe 'Islop singin' it in Manchester. An' me aht of a job— ME—wots the best blinkin' " Messiah " in the business ! ! ' "

They had reached the Palace Pier, paid the toll and passed those contraptions of simple fun which enable the great pleasure-loving public to see—at the cost of one penny—a miniature execution shed with a parson doll, a condemned murderer doll, and lots of warden dolls all doing their stuff in spasmodic jerks to the tolling of the passing bell. If in the mood for further carnival, a penny will secure the portrait of a future wife (or husband). Most patrons are content with the other kind of execution.

" Good lord, look at that ! " exclaimed Edward.

" Look at what ? "

" At that man there, with the thing dangling from the brim of his hat."

Yes, it was a hat-guard, a black cord stretching from the hat, technically known as the " Gent's straw boater " to the lapel of the coat.

" When did you last see a hat guard ? " asked Edward. " Not for years ? I thought not. I haven't seen one, either. Gone are the gadgets of yester-year."

" Yes, indeed, all of them, even moustache-cups have gone, and it's odd, because there are still quite a few moustaches about. Good lord, though, I haven't thought of those extra-ordinary inventions for twenty years and more—you remember 'em, cups with a sort of extra rim as a barrier to prevent white moustaches getting tea or coffee stained. Those were the days when people trained hair on their upper lips to look like the back of a watering cart . . . weren't they, Edward ? "

" Fortunately, we regard sinister moustaches as comic nowadays—associated with Old Bill and Harry Tate, who has had more fun with a moustache than any other actor living."

" Ah ! " rambled on Alf. " I knew a grand actor who, on one occasion, didn't find the moustache question very funny—it was a man I loved—Gerald du Maurier. When Gerald joined up as a cadet in the latter part of the War, his battalion of budding Guards' officers was on parade one morning at Watford, and was addressed on the subject of hair growing by the Colonel. ' I want every cadet who *can* grow a moustache to do so,' he said. ' I don't want you to look like a lot of silly actors ! ' Dear Gerald, the touchiest of men on the subject of the honour and dignity of the theatrical profession, raged inwardly, and the scowl of an old-time tragedian fixed itself on his face. But he had to stand to attention and listen. ' War hath her tragedies no less than Peace '."

" Yes. And the War was the dividing line between two phases of existence, both in big and little things. We won't talk of the big things on a sunny Sunday morning on Brighton pier. Let's return to the lost gadgets. The War knocked out sovereign purses, for instance. I should think the makers of sovereign purses to-day do about as lavish a trade as the manufacturers of smoked glasses for viewing total eclipses of the sun."

" And dance programmes. Is there even a remote suburb or sleepy cathedral city where, at a dance, a man dons white gloves and, armed with a dance programme from which dangles a tiny pencil, approaches some young damsel with a bow, and says : ' May I have the pleasure of No. 11—it's a polka ? ' "

" I doubt it," said Alf. " But the change is all to the good, except the gloves. When I see a man place what looks like a hot ham round the small of a girl's back, I often think white gloves should not nowadays, like good manners, be confined to potmen."

" Are you sure good manners have really been dropped ? I'm more of an optimist on this point than you. Unnecessary forms of politeness—long, insincere speeches, flowery compliments, leaving visiting cards, and so forth—have gone simply because there isn't time for them. What's more, they are not needed in 1938 any more than most of our disused gadgets are needed. Those odd devices of gold-ware which kept ties from rucking up over stiff ' all-round ' collars have gone because such collars have gone, and a good job, too. Travelling caps (you remember, Sherlock Holmes wore one?) have gone because railway carriages are better heated, and we no longer have to burn the sides of our shoes on foot-warmers (also departed) while the rest of our bodies shivered. Travelling lamps have gone, because railway carriages are better lighted. Cab whistles have gone out (one blast for a hansom and two for a four-wheeler) for the best of reasons—they are forbidden.

"But I miss the hansoms," said Edward, "although you had to be careful what you said—or did—when you were with a female companion. The old cabbies must have learned—and seen—a lot through that little trap-door in the roof. There are still a few left in London—six, I believe. How the drivers live I can't imagine; probably on sentimental and slightly alcoholic lovers of the old days, just because they *were* the old days. What's left of the hansoms don't do any harm. But it would be just as sensible and as silly to keep up a rank of sedan-chairs in Leicester Square. We must move with the times, old man."

"We must move from here, anyway," said Alf. "It's ten past one, and I'm hungry. The sea air always makes me so ravenous I could eat a dead horse for lunch."

"You probably will."

The two friends walked landwards along an almost deserted pier. Brighton, residents and visitors alike, were busy with the Sunday joint. Customs may change, gadgets may be dropped, wars muddled through, and peaces muddled still more sadly; but the Sunday joint at midday remains for Britons an established fact by a changeless decree.

In the hotel lounge, fortunately orchestra-less, there was peace as cocktails were ordered. To a small table in a corner a group of early lunchers had adjourned for coffee and cigars, and some of them were drinking port.

"Why do English people drink port after a meal, and the French drink port before a meal?" asked Alf.

"Why do clergymen fasten their collars at the back, while you and I fasten ours in front?" asked Edward, in reply. "It's all a matter of taste. And, thank goodness, tastes differ, or, as Sam Weller said, 'What would happen to the makers of fancy veskits'?"

Having finished their cocktails, which, as Alf put it, should have been called "The Hairdressers' Dream," being as they were strong enough to grow hair on even the most sophisticated tonsils, the pair sat down to lunch—off lobsters which seemed to have spent most of their leisure in reclining on ice, Southdown mutton which had taken the trouble to come to the Mother Country all the way from New Zealand, and tinned peaches on which Melba had never set eyes. The conversation turned again to the old days and London as it was in the late 'eighties.

"I suppose," said Edward, "Piccadilly Circus is absolutely the centre of the world, isn't it?"

"Of course it is, dear fellow, and now that it has gone automatic it seems to me like looking at one's Grandmother —after she has had her face lifted. The change is extraordinary. When did you first see what is now the Scotsman's Cinema, Alf?"

"It was in 1885, old man, that I first trundled into the Magic Circle on the top of an old knife-board omnibus—a crazy conveyance filled with straw which was strewn on the floor to keep one's feet warm, and while the interior was lit by acetylene lamps, the 'bus itself was drawn by a set of lean horses."

"And no motor-cars, Alf?"

"Motor-cars!" said the old explorer. "They were as little dreamed of in those days as television or radio. Com-

pared with to-day, Piccadilly Circus was a sleepy hollow
minus its Heindrick Hudson. On every street corner boot-
blacks cried ' Shine, sir ; only a penny ! ' Newspaper boys
sold the *Globe* and *Westminster Gazette*, in which you were lucky
if you could find the day-before-yesterday's news. Flower
girls offered you nosegays at twopence each ' for the pretty lady,'
if you happened to be with one ; and crossing sweepers swept
a path before you, while they touched their caps, giving an
imitation of the famous Baxter print, ' Copper, your honour.' "

" Baxter prints ! " said Edward. " I love them ; I had a
lot once, but they were disappointing as assets, for when I
was obliged to sell them I got less than half I paid for them."

" Well, of course you did," said Alf. " There happens
to be a ring ; but they *are* very beautiful. It is funny to
think that some of these prints which were published at five
shillings are catalogued to-day at thirty pounds. I don't
know if you know it, my dear Edward," said Alf, " but
Baxter conceived the idea of reproducing masterpieces in a
cheap form, so that poor people could have pictures in their
homes. But we were talking of Piccadilly, not Baxter,
weren't we ? I'll tell you what was rather a jolly sight.
On Christmas Eve the Rothschilds always sent to every bus
man in London a brace of pheasants which the drivers used
to hang proudly from their seats.

" My goodness, though," went on Alf, " talking of driving,
what a perfect muddle there would be to-day if the traffic
was uncontrolled as it used to be."

" Do you mean to say," asked Edward, " that everybody
could drive where they liked ? "

" Yes, rather ! " said Alf. " Hansom cabs and four-
wheelers drove crossways and sideways, backwards and
forwards, into each other, and sometimes over each other.

Horses fell, and were either taken out of the shafts, or whipped to their feet; and all this to an orchestra of whistlings for conveyances by porters, or by pedestrians, many of whom used their own private whistles, attached to their own particular key chains."

"And what was the Circus like at night-time?" asked Edward.

"Fairly dull," said Alf. "Gas lamps flickered dimly over the scene, for the new marvel 'Rogers' Electric Light' had only just come into being, and was considered little more than a joke to create laughter at pantomime time. The ladies of the day saved the Westminster Council considerable money by sweeping the pavements with their trailing skirts; while the Lads of the Village, called 'La-di-dahs,' sauntered idly to the Bodega, which was not far from Scott's Fish Emporium, the most fashionable oyster bar in the West End. At night-time, where Eros now stands, there used to be a coffee-stall on wheels."

"Really! I suppose most of the buildings are the same though, aren't they?" inquired Edward.

"Oh, Lord, no!" said Alf. "The Pavilion, of course, is a reminder of the Circus's former doubtful glories, and was the premier Music Hall in London. Within its walls a chairman announced nightly that 'the next artist to appear again' would be—either the Great MacDermott, Charles Godfrey, Herbert Campbell, Vance, Bessie Bellwood, Jenny Hill (the Vital Spark), or some other of the host of idols of the 'Alls.

"It was at the Pavilion that Albert Chevalier made his first music-hall appearance, singing the songs which made him famous. I knew him well," said Alf, "and a more unassuming or charming man it would be impossible to imagine. He never seemed to realise even when London was at his feet, that he was anybody in particular. Of course, the Criterion is just as it was, and it is funny to remember that Messrs. Spiers & Pond built the Criterion Theatre not that they should make money out of it as a theatre; they did so in the hope that the people who attended the performances would patronise their restaurant for dinner before the play, and go to supper afterwards. The little House was one of the few theatres in which, on entering, one went down some flights of stairs to the stalls, and this fact caused a wit of the time to remark ' Good heavens ! If there is a fire in this theatre, we shall have to climb for two hours to get out, and then probably find ourselves sitting on Spiers & Pond's grill.'

" In the days I am talking about, the long bar of the Criterion Restaurant was a famous place frequented by ' The Boys,' members of a community who agreed with Arthur Orton, of Tichborne fame, that people who had ' no brains and plenty of money were made for people who had plenty of brains and no money.'

" A well-known object in the West End," said Alf, " was the Piccadilly goat."

" What on earth was that ? " said Edward.

" It was a large white animal," said Alf, " that roamed about Piccadilly and the Circus, and for which the policemen very often held up the traffic. It belonged to one of the Rothschild family, I think, and lived in a stable somewhere off Stratton Street."

" Well, it would not have much of a chance to-day, would it ? " said Edward.

" You're telling me," said Alf. " But, thinking backwards, it is very hard to visualise the Circus without Eros. I remember being driven on a foggy November night by Alfred Gilbert, the sculptor, in company with the mighty Henry Irving, Arthur Pinero, and J. L. Toole, to peep behind a huge awning which hid from view Gilbert's soon-to-be-unveiled masterpiece, that has for so many years looked down tolerantly on the frailties of men and women. Sometimes the atmosphere of the Circus was brighter when a four-in-hand with yellow wheels would clatter across it towards the Park, its driver no less a personage than the famous Lord Londesborough, his eyes protected by large black goggles. Here, too, very often might be seen the Marquis of Ailesbury, with a purple face surmounted by a cabman's top hat; while for his personal pleasure and comfort he affected a heavily-pleated box-cloth driving coat possessed of buttons as large as oyster shells. His titles in Burke's Peerage, I think, occupied an inch of that bible dedicated to the Debility and Gentry, but he was eccentric and impossible to the last.

"Jane Cakebread was a well-known figure in the Circus; a happy-go-lucky drunkard who, before she died, had succeeded in being sentenced for disorderly conduct over a hundred and twenty times.

"It seems strange to remember that there was practically no night-life in Piccadilly in 1885—night-life, I mean, as we know it to-day. It was little more than a meeting-place for ill-assorted couples in ill-lit corners. Between the hours of eleven and twelve it was a clearing-house for those who caught their buses for the then far-distant Earl's Court and St. John's Wood, or the many who hurried through it towards Charing Cross, there to take the smoke-laden, choking Underground to some such country place as Hammersmith. The Circus, on Boat Race nights, was one in which the four-wheelers were overturned, much to the delight of their drivers, for the light and dark blues of that period—sober or not—never failed to give the owners of these ramshackle contraptions a fiver for the fun they had had at their expense.

"Gone are the lamp-posts; gone are the characters; gone are the growlers and a dozen other things which the 'seventies no doubt imagined were the last word in gaiety when they saw them in the eighties; and, in their place, we have Din, Glare, Hustle and Hurry.

"Are we better off with our luxurious, hectic non-stop rush and bustle? Are we? I often wonder, dear Edward."

"Oh! If you had to go back to it, Alf, you'd go mad."

"I wasn't talking about going back to it, dear fellow—I asked, 'Are we better off?'"

"You can never live anything over again," sagely remarked Edward. "Places revisited, and women who were troublesome rekissed after long absences—are things that don't make sense."

"Of course, mind you, there was plenty of fun to be had in the 'eighties if you knew where to go for it. The old Corinthian Club, for instance, off Jermyn Street, was a gay, amusing—though disreputable—dancing establishment, while the Gardenia, in Leicester Square, though not—as the Americans say—'so swell' was, also, a place where Cupid's cards of introduction were gold pieces on which, strangely enough, the head of good Queen Victoria appeared. I hope it never came to the knowledge of that August Lady the base uses her coins were put to at midnight.

"The Continental, of course, for supper was *the* place of all others to which the Jeûnesse Stage Dorée found their way when seeking the companionship of the *demi-monde* of Heaven. It was the home of beautifully-dressed ladies and bad champagne. A wit remarked of St. John's Wood: 'London is bounded on the north by St. John's Wood—and I'm glad of it.' This being because it was in this salubrious suburb that all the female *habituées* of the Continental lived and dyed.

# NIGHT LIGHTS

" I suppose ' Jimmies,' as the St. James's Restaurant was known, was certainly the rowdiest of all the smart supper haunts frequented by the night-birds. There were fewer ladies to be met with there, but certainly more fashionable male inebriates than anywhere else in Town. Many a time have I seen all the lights turned out at two in the morning by some enterprising youth who, being as he felt a humorist, proceeded to throw a hundred hats into the darkness which created absolute pandemonium, when their owners tried to retrieve their head wear.

" Here, too, battles—with oyster shells as the ammunition—were not of uncommon occurrence, during which, if you were wise, you crawled under your table. The night-life of London in those days was inside, and not outside, as it is now. Then, again, if you knew where to go, cock-fights could be seen, and many a main was fought not a hundred miles from St. James's Street, while during one season at the old Gaiety Theatre, Hughie Drummond—a great figure of the period—installed a rat pit for the amusement of a favourite actress and her friends after supper.

" The old Pelican Club flourished into the 'nineties, and was the haunt of all the most amusing men in Town. Here, one met noblemen and famous actors, musicians, authors, stockbrokers and poets—most of them Wits, and many who lived by them. Clubs were Clubs in those days, and the brilliant dialogue of their suppers invariably garnished the luncheon tables of the Town.

" Ladies went to bed early in the 'eighties ; their Lords— but not necessarily their Masters—making use of their latch-keys to the rattle of the milk cans.

" For a real Club man to have gone to bed before three or four in the morning was as unheard of as a hen laying an ostrich egg.

# TALK, IDLE TALK

" I think, Edward," said Alf, who had been almost talking to himself for a quarter of an hour, " the one thing I regret more than anything else, is the passing of those happy hours spent in Clubland after midnight, for with them wit has vanished, and the cradles of real characters remain empty."

## " THE NOBLE ART "

Seated one night at the ring-side (this line is written with apologies to the late Sir Arthur Sullivan), Alf and Edward were watching the modern millionaires whose lawyers arrange that they are to knock each other about for a few thousand pounds a round, wondering whether it had been arranged that the contract for the film rights of the big fight would compel the gallant heavyweights to refrain from becoming horizontal before the sixth round. Alas, many a time had they occupied the same seats in that vast hall where they were now sitting, ignorant beyond words of the politics of the ring. How often had they seen Joe Beckett give an imitation of his famous ancestor, who took the count at Canterbury. How often had they seen Phil Scott the fireman meet some one who wasn't a fireman but who did to Scott what Scott had done to London conflagrations. Many a time had they joined in the old-time chorus of that famous ditty, " Waltz me around again, Willie," as the gladiators, mistaking each other for long lost brothers, opened their welcoming arms to murmur into willing ears on to which part of the floor they intended for their mother's sake to lie and listen to the number so dear to the heart of the pugilist—the Magic Ten.

On this particular night, however, they were lucky, for they had just witnessed Mr. Thomas Farr put the amusing Mr. Max Baer to bed and tuck him up anything but tenderly. Well pleased with the thought that perhaps at last they had discovered a heavyweight, the two friends drove to the best grill room in London and, biting a few oysters, chatted on. " I know, dear Edward," said Alf, " that you never used to go to the old National, and by not doing so you have missed a jugful because while in the immense building we have just left you are only a numbered ticket, there, in the congested intimacy of the surroundings, you had the sort of uplift that not only were you a blood, but a patron and a sportsman and, indeed, almost a gentleman if you permitted yourself to dabble in fiction after dinner. It was in the seats near the timekeeper and to his right and left were to be seen those privileged to sit in the chairs which bore their names, these being the life members of the Club. While on every side sat the most knowledgeable sporting men of the day, who of course knew all about boxing for the very good reason that most of them had never put on anything but kid gloves.

" Please don't imagine, my dear Edward, that in referring to the ignorant in white kid gloves I forget that seated near them were some of the greatest sporting figures that ever lived. Men to whom even the princely Toms and Jerrys of the Corinthian period would have gladly doffed their beavers. What a downright splendid specimen of an English gentleman, for instance, was Sir Claude de Crespigny, with a face fashioned out of Empire oak and a chin and jaw which almost inquired where there might be a spot of trouble on which to adjudicate or take part in. ' No nonsense ' was surely his motto, as a great hulking Covent Garden porter found to his cost one evening, when he bumped heavily into the Sporting Baronet as he was coming out of the Tavistock Hotel. This worthy, instead of apologising, started to remember all the oaths that had been handed down to him as heirlooms, which so enraged Sir Claude that, without making the slightest fuss, he handed his coat to a companion and proceeded to provide a bed on the pavement for the gentleman who had, no doubt, made up his mind that his grandchildren should graduate at Borstal. The fact that I mention this episode is not to give undue credit to a white tie and dress waistcoat. I do so because it must be of interest to you, dear Edward, to know that Sir Claude de Crespigny at that time was seventy years of age.

"And that grand old gentleman, too, Lord Lonsdale, was as much part of the National Sporting Club all his life as were the boxers themselves. You can see him to-day, walking in the Park with a couple of golden labradors and a red setter or two, debonair and jaunty, carrying his eighty years as lightly as he holds his inevitable cigar. It will take very little to convince you, I'm sure, dear fellow, what a picture he was as he stood at the ringside in the eighties, the ideal Patron of a truly British sport."

"I can quite gather he did," said Edward.

"Mind you," continued Alf, "I don't say for a minute that London does not possess its prototypes of bygone days; it does, but look at them as you may, they seem to be only the products of the black and white artist and not the colourful characters whom we visualize as the patrons of a Mendoza, a Black Sam, a Sayers or a Mace. I'm afraid real glamour has gone from the Prize Ring, old boy. Wagering never killed a sport, but huge purses may. 'Never back anything that can talk,' is an old adage, and when we know that talkers are sometimes promoters who, cursing each other in print by day, share each other's cigars when night has fallen, one must not be accused of being over optimistic when one perhaps wonders if there may not be slightly intensive discussions as to the ways and means to best provide for the dependants of some of these worthies. This never occurred at the old Club, and needless to say does not happen at the National, which has taken its place at Earl's Court to-day, while at Wembley also you can witness some of the grandest boxing in the world.

"Oh, yes!" mused Alf, as he thought aloud backwards, "the old National was full of characters; Peggy Bettison, for instance, the most famous of all its managers, was a card and no mistake. If you get a chance, Edward, have a look at George Belcher's picture of him, in that artist's wonderful ring series. He looks as if he had on trousers belonging to a man twice his size. I often used to think they were coming down when he stepped over the ropes to announce a decision. The timekeeper, who sat with his top hat on all night, was also a real type. I think he was a Greek. A smart, alert little man who, I fancy, like Gene Corri, was on the Stock Exchange. Old Mr. Douglas, the father of the famous cricketer, refereed a thousand fights in the old days, and would order a man out of the ring after he had been twice cautioned in less than no time if he suspected there was what in the vernacular is called 'Hank' of any kind going on."

"I knew his son well," said Edward.

"Did you?"

"My goodness, no man living ever stonewalled as he did if he felt tactics demanded it, Alf."

"No. I remember him driving the Australians mad in the Test Matches at Sydney," said Alf. "On one occasion he took an hour and a half to make eight runs. The crowd on the Hill booed and barracked, but he took not the slightest notice. I think it was during the season that he captained England in the Antipodes that his initials being J. W. H. T. Douglas, he was christened by the crowd ' Johnny Won't Hit To-day Douglas.'

"One of the most interesting things at the old National

was to look at the boxers who were not engaged in the evening's sport, sitting together on benches raised one above the other, on the stage itself. Most of them were well-known figures and many of them watched the boxing with more than ordinary interest, being probably matched to meet the winners of the contests. There was no greater character anywhere there than old Bat Mullins. He taught me what boxing I know, and was unique. A staunch Roman Catholic, he went to Mass every morning, carrying his boxing gloves in a little bag if he was on his way to give a lesson. He was the last of the old knuckle fighters, and had fought fifty-two battles with bare fists. He was a quiet and most respectable old man and full of wise advice, a favourable admonition to his pupils when asked what was the best thing to do in a street fight being, ' Well, sir, if you knocks your man down, stand over him and have a good look, and if he starts to get up, run like an 'are, you've got a good 'un.'

" I don't remember how many people the old Club held, but few, of course, compared with Wembley," said Alf. The hall was really a theatre, for it had a gallery at one end and a stage at the other, while the ring itself was set in the middle of the stalls.

" In the days it pleases me to remember," continued Alf, " boxers had not gone in for literature and the word ' journalist' would have probably meant to them a journeyman who took on all comers at travelling booths. The old time pugs were interviewed only by their opponents, after the gong had gone, and were not encouraged by the Press, as they are to-day, to be photographed playing cats' cradle with fair-haired little children, nor did they tell the world that they intended eating their opponent for supper, prior to visiting some well-known night club, the name of which they had gone to a Berlitz School to learn how to pronounce. The 'eighties were the days of the real tough nuts. Men who preferred to slumber in their homes at Wapping rather than become Sleeping Beauties in public."

" Evidently, old man," said Edward, " you are off with the new gloves and on with the old."

" Of course I am," replied Alf, " for you mustn't forget that my days were the days of Peter Jackson, J. L. Sullivan, Charlie Mitchell, Slavin, Jeffreys, Jim Corbett, Bob Fitzsimmons, Jack Johnson, Jim Driscoll and Pedlar Palmer—I saw them all box—and bar Dempsey and Tunney, and they are of yesterday—there is no one to-day in the heavyweight class to compare with Jackson, Johnson, Jefferys, Corbett, Fitzsimmons, as masters, Sullivan and Slavin as sloggers, or Jim Driscoll and Pedlar Palmer—Driscoll, of course, being one of the most beautiful two-handed fighters that ever stepped into a ring."

" You never saw anyone so good as Jimmy Wilde, though, in his class, did you, Alf ? "

" Good heavens, no ! A wonder of wonders and het bravest of the brave ! The night he gave away nearly two stone to Pete Harman—and was beaten—will always remain for me a sorrowful and tragic memory."

" Old Bob Fitzsimmons was a grand man, and no greater general ever stepped through the ropes than this Cornishman from the sleepy little town of Helston. His ginger-coloured hair became scanty at the age of thirty, this giving him the appearance of a man many years older. He had huge, rather rounded shoulders, and his powerful torso was supported by what appeared to be the legs of a weakling ; the length of his arms was abnormal—he was able, without bending, to scratch those legs well below the knees.

" It was Fitzsimmons who invented a new method of

delivering the solar plexus punch; he used to step to the left right across his man and hand it to him with his right. Battle after battle he won with this novel and daring method of attack. For cunning and ring craft he has had few equals, and I doubt if ever a superior. It was Lord Londsale who discovered Peter Jackson, and I remember hearing him say that he considered him to be the best heavyweight he had ever seen—illustrating verbally Jackson's wonderful judgment of distance by explaining that he could shadow box at a cork placed on the top of a champagne bottle and, leading at it with left or right, could touch it without dislodging it.

" He stayed at Lowther on several occasions and I several times heard that great sporting nobleman loud in praise of the perfect way he always behaved. In the ring Jackson looked like an ebony panther and moved with a swiftness and grace which are indescribable.

" Charlie Mitchell, one gathers from real judges, was among heavyweights one of the best British boxers that ever stepped—and must have been extremely like Jackson and also Johnson in his lightning-like use of his hands and quick, clean break-away and come-back.

" Jim Corbett was another of this class of picture-book to watch—I saw him fight Jeffreys in New York in 1890. It was one of the most interesting contests I ever saw. For nineteen rounds, Jeffreys, heavy, hairy chested and looking like a bear that had lost its keeper, followed the volatile Jim doggedly round the ring, the spectators conscious that while Corbett was hitting him how, when and where he liked, Jeffreys was waiting with a crashing right hand. In the twentieth round the opportunity came and Corbett, who had been laughing at and talking back to Mrs. Jeffreys, who was making objectionable remarks to him every time he hit her husband, was carried insensible to his dressing-room. Jeffreys was a boiler-maker by trade, a man of immense strength, who at one time had been Corbett's sparring partner.

"Years afterwards I met Corbett in London and, talking over this—to him, fatal evening—I asked him how it happened. All he said was, 'I don't know. I was sitting in my corner at the end of the nineteenth round, thinking what my posters would look like in a play called "Gentleman Joe" I was to open with in Chicago a month later, when I woke up in my dressing-room. I guess I got careless and walked right into it.' Corbett was a delightful man ; he started life as a clerk in a bank and, curiously enough, unlike most prize-fighters, had remarkably expressive and attractive hands. I never saw J. L. Sullivan except once in his saloon at Boston —he had retired from the game, having lost his crown to Charlie Mitchell, who had danced round him, and to the bewilderment of the undefeated champion and Americans in general, made an absolute monkey of him.

"On the occasion of which I speak I was seated having a drink with a rather fat, inoffensive, unathletic actor friend, when a mountain of a man lurched over our table and leaning across it swept our glasses on-to the floor. My friend, very rightly incensed, slapped the gentleman across the face, who, being off his balance, crashed under the table. In a moment the bar was in an uproar, and we were told if we wanted to save our lives we'd better bolt, for the giant who was scrambling to his feet was J. L. Sullivan. Need I say, dear Edward, that we were both outside like flashes of greased lightning."

"Oh, well ! " said Edward, " the old order changeth, and perhaps it's just as well, or the percussion cap and ramrod would not have given way to the hammerless ejector."

" Yes," agreed Alf, " and when you come to think of it, if the charming present-day debutante has learned to lisp that fine old English word ' lousy ' so prettily, and with her grandmother patronises those really refined Social Functions, the Bottle Parties of Mayfair, why should not the Bruiser take unto himself a Dinner Jacket ? "

## ALF AND EDWARD GO HOME.

It was a beautiful night, and instead of taking a taxi, Alf and Edward walked towards Admiralty Arch, sauntered homewards through the Park towards the turning which would take them past St. James's Palace, up St. James's Street, into Piccadilly and so to the flat in Clarges Street.

The moon at its full seemed to be smiling and well content as it wrapped the heart of our great Empire in a protecting cloak of midnight silver.

The glow of the City lights to North and South and East and West was only faintly visible, for the windows of a million tired souls had gently fallen.

In the not so far distance a Nation's Meeting Place, the Great House of England, stood clear and impregnable against the sky. What shouts of triumph had not its grey walls heard. What tears of sorrow had not its iron gates seen shed. There Kings and Queens had slept and here to-night the Father of his people and his Queen were resting.

" A wonderful country, Edward, my boy."

" I should say so," said Edward, " and lucky beyond words to have so fine a pair to love as we have."

They stood a moment and in silence raised their hats. The simple homage of two ordinary men. It was the pledge of many millions, meaning as it does

# NIGHT LIGHTS

## FOR EVER AND EVER.

An hour later, seated in one of the arm-chairs which had been the birthplace of so many profound questions, Alf suddenly said : " Whom would you vote the greatest British Queen who ever lived ? "

" O, Lord knows ! " answered the simple one, " Elizabeth perhaps . . . Queen Victoria, I suppose. I have never thought very much about it. How do you mean, great, Alf ? As Empire Builder or Statesman, or what ? "

" I was thinking not so much," replied Alf, " of the things which the historian seizes on—the signing of treaties, the introduction of reforms or the imposing of a personality. I was thinking of greatness in its simple and most splendid sense. Thinking of one who has stood for Britain always. Laughed with Her. Sorrowed with Her. Toiled for Her and given her Life for Her. One who, in her age, has stood like some great captain watching with loving eyes the Youthful Hand which steers the ship of State. What greater Queen than she ? Is not my question answered ? "

As Edward spoke his eye wandered towards a painting on the wall, a picture of a ship, majestic and supreme. The most magnificent in all the world. " ' The Might of England,' that, my friend! How proud it would be if it knew it bore Her NAME."

And so the Two talked on and are still talking, as men will always talk of Life and Love and other things. Their conversation a *poussé-café* of Sense and Nonsense.

" I wonder," said the Journalist, " if I set down on paper all that we've discussed during these last few months, whether anyone would read it ? "

" I don't think so," said Edward.

" You never can tell," said Alf, " to-day the weak-minded are by no means in a minority."

# APPENDIX OF NAMES

# APPENDIX OF NAMES

244